*Bighorn sheep rams on Mount Everts in Yellowstone National Park. Photo by Jacob Frank, National Park Service.*

# Greater Yellowstone's Mountain Ungulates

**A** CONTRAST IN MANAGEMENT HISTORIES AND CHALLENGES

Library of Congress Control Number: 2021911281

ISBN: 978-0-578-92639-1

# Greater Yellowstone's Mountain Ungulates

**A** CONTRAST IN MANAGEMENT HISTORIES AND CHALLENGES

*Editors:*

*P.J. White, Robert A. Garrott and Douglas E. McWhirter*

*Contributing Authors*

*Carson J. Butler, Julie A. Cunningham, Jesse D. DeVoe, Sarah R. Dewey,*

*Elizabeth P. Flesch, Tabitha A. Graves, Blake Lowrey, Hollie M. Miyasaki,*

*Kevin Monteith, Kerry M. Murphy, Andrew C. Pils, Kelly M. Proffitt,*

*Jay J. Rotella, Daniel B. Tyers, Mary E. Wood*

*Featuring the photography of Mark Gocke.*

*Technical Editor: Lorelyn Mayr, Media Works, LLC, Bozeman, Montana*

# Contents

# Preface

*Kevin P. Hurley, Vice-President for Conservation,*
*Wild Sheep Foundation*

Greater Yellowstone. I hope every reader has one or more special places that touch their heart, their mind, their core. For me, the Greater Yellowstone is one of my places. For more than 40 years, I've had the good fortune to live, work, play, raise a family, and engage in the conservation bio-politics of the states of Wyoming, Montana, and Idaho. The heart, and the center, of this tri-state region is the Greater Yellowstone.

While these may be spots on a map to some, for me, every one of these locations triggers a memory, an experience, a discovery, a connection, a vivid recollection. Absaroka Range. Trout Peak. Hurricane Mesa. Whirlwind Peak. Thorofare Plateau. Gallatin Crest. Lionshead. Rattlesnake Mountain. Wapiti Ridge. Electric Peak. Washakie Wilderness. Paradise Valley. The Trident. Hyalite. Rhyolite. Obsidian Cliff. Hawk's Rest. Island Park. Pilot. Index. West Yellowstone. Firehole River. The Thunderer. Sunlight Basin. Sleeping Giant. Two Ocean Plateau. Bechler. Heart Lake. Eagle Creek Meadows. Barronette Peak. Tower Falls. Hellroaring Mountain. Hardluck Mountain. Shoshone Plateau.

Slough Creek. Dunraven Pass. Quake Lake. Hebgen Lake. Beartooth Plateau. Stillwater. Quintuple Peaks. Red Lodge. Big Game Ridge. Cooke City. Carter Mountain. The Grand. Mount Moran. Ram Pasture. Clarks Fork Canyon. Upper Lamar. On and on. So many places, so many experiences, so many memories. I'm humbled by the scope, scale, and resources of the Greater Yellowstone.

I continually pay respect to the world's first national park, the incredible geologic features resulting from the subterranean forces that shaped this region, the myriad high lakes and rushing rivers, the towering peaks, the relentless wind, the endless blue skies, and all the natural forces and features that make the Greater Yellowstone what it is. For me, the absolute topping for this supernatural dessert is the abundant and diverse wildlife that seasonally, or year-round, know this place as home.

From the most studied grizzlies on the planet, to the trumpeter swans and bald eagles that return each summer, from the gray wolves that again course these valleys to the Yellowstone cutthroat trout that rise in its crystal-clear waters, and from the last bastion of pure bison to the migratory herds of elk that disperse along ancient pathways to survive brutal winters, for me, it's the wildlife that makes the Greater Yellowstone so great. My personal favorites, and my career-long focus, are the mountain sheep that thrive in the Greater Yellowstone.

For nearly 10,000 years, the Tukudeka or Mountain Shoshone people, commonly referred to as the Sheep Eater Indians, carved out a unique existence, utilizing every part of the mountain sheep they were clever enough and fortunate enough to harvest. Scattered throughout the Greater Yellowstone are jack-strawed remnants of drive traps and catch pits where Sheep Eater Indians caught, killed, and processed mountain sheep. Food, clothing, tools, and weapons (including powerful longbows made from laminated bighorn sheep horns, after soaking in accessible thermal features) were all derived from harvested mountain sheep. Petroglyphs and pictographs etched into prominent rock faces and varnished outcrops bear witness to the abundance of mountain sheep historically found in the Greater Yellowstone.

Larger-than-life mountain men like John Coulter and Osborne Russell wrote of the "endless numbers" of mountain sheep they encountered, and quite likely survived on. Along the eastern edge of what is now recognized as Yellowstone National Park, the Absaroka Range has been a stronghold for mountain sheep throughout recorded time. Almost 80 years ago, in their 1942 Wyoming Technical Report, Ralph Honess and Nedward Frost noted the abundance of mountain sheep in the Greater Yellowstone. Twenty years later, in his classic monograph on "Bighorn Sheep of the United States," Helmut Buechner reinforced the importance of the Absaroka Range to mountain sheep. After 40+ years, I still don't know anywhere that rivals the bighorn sheep numbers found in the Absarokas.

About the same time that Honess and Frost published their 1942 report, what was then known as the Montana Fish and Game Department introduced mountain goats into the Beartooth Mountains, along the Wyoming/Montana line. Idaho Fish and Game Department followed suit, introducing mountain goats into the Palisades country along the Snake River in 1967 and 1969. While paleontological evidence shows what was called Harrington's mountain goat in Wyoming's Big Horn Mountains more than 14,000 years ago, contemporary knowledge indicates mountain goats were not present in the Greater Yellowstone when early explorers, historical and mountain man journals, railroad expedition diaries, and observations of the Greater Yellowstone's wildlife were more formally recorded.

Suffice it to say that mountain goats are now widely established in the Greater Yellowstone; some would say super-imposed on top of the region's native bighorn sheep. Personally, I favor country wild enough to support both alpine dwellers. But, like many wildlife species, and even with so much wilderness and remote backcountry, management is a necessity.

If my diary and recall are clear, in mid-October 2009, along with my longtime friend and Wyoming Game and Fish Department co-worker Doug McWhirter, I drove through a huge slice of the Greater Yellowstone, from Cody to Mammoth,

Yellowstone National Park, to sit down with Glenn Plumb and P. J. White of the National Park Service, and Bob Garrott of Montana State University. Our shared purpose was to launch the notion of a bighorn sheep and mountain goat research project in and around Yellowstone and Grand Teton national parks, in conjunction with the state wildlife agencies for Wyoming, Montana, and Idaho, and the Forest Service. Thoughts and words evolved into actions, with one of the first tangible steps being to scour the wildlife observation systems of three state wildlife agencies and two national parks, along with Forest Service wildlife records.

Much like analyzing ripples created from dropping a pebble into a pond, early efforts focused on mapping mountain goat observations in the Greater Yellowstone, by decade. High-tech geographic information system (GIS) maps of mountain goat observations were generated and overlaid with bighorn sheep observations recorded by the state and federal agencies, along with other credible records. Looking back over almost eight decades of mountain goat observations, researchers with the Greater Yellowstone Mountain Ungulate Project were able to reconstruct how mountain goats arrived at their current numbers and distribution.

With incredible field effort and technological savvy, a succession of research-ers, graduate students, and their field technicians collected and analyzed fine-scale habitat selection data for both bighorn sheep and mountain goats in the Greater Yellowstone. Armed with that knowledge, project researchers were then able to crys-tal-ball 50 to 80 years into the future to gauge and estimate the potential number and distribution of mountain goats juxtaposed with known distribution of native mountain sheep. The analysis, modeling, and projections are fascinating!

The chapters in this Greater Yellowstone Mountain Ungulate Project book, written by an incredibly-talented team of skilled and experienced wildlife biolo-gists, provide a fascinating glimpse into the past, present and future of one of the most special places on Earth, the Greater Yellowstone. Wildlife management is not an easy task. Wildlife and land/resource management professionals need to look back, carefully mine and consider historical data and recorded observations, and develop their best recommendations going forward. I can only express my sincere gratitude and appreciation for the talented biologists who took on this monumental effort. The Greater Yellowstone will benefit from their dedication and efforts.

I feel incredibly fortunate for 40+ years of wildlife experiences in the Greater Yellowstone. I am incredibly humbled to have been asked to write this Foreword. Many thanks and my enduring respect for those who did the heavy lifting on this important mountain ungulate project.

*Kevin Hurley with bighorn sheep ram near the South Fork Shoshone River, Wyoming, 1985.*

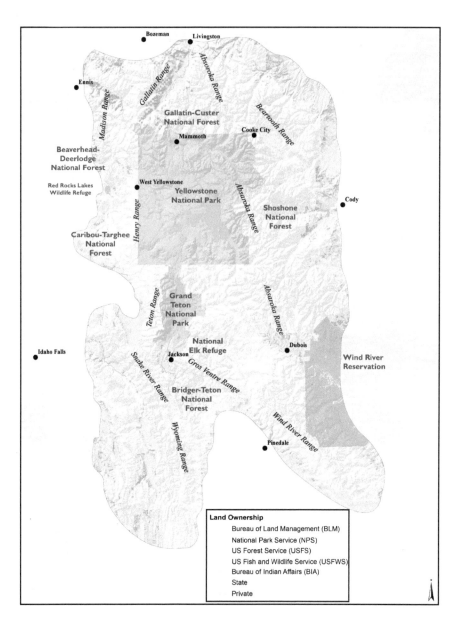

Figure 1. The Greater Yellowstone Area. Land management agencies are the Forest Service (USFS), Bureau of Land Management (BLM), Fish and Wildlife Service (FWS), and National Park Service (NPS). Private, state, and tribal lands are shaded in gray. Map by Howard Williams, National Park Service.

# Introduction

*P. J. White, Robert A. Garrott,*
*and Douglas E. McWhirter*

The Greater Yellowstone Area, which includes portions of Idaho, Montana, and Wyoming (Figure 1), is an important region for bighorn sheep (*Ovis canadensis*) in North America. During the 1990s, descendants of mountain goats (*Oreamnos americanus*) brought into the area during the 1940s and 1950s moved into northern portions of Yellowstone National Park through the Absaroka and Gallatin mountain ranges in Montana. Mountain goat numbers increased during the following decades and goats moved southward into a primary range for bighorn sheep along the eastern boundary of the park in the Absaroka and Beartooth ranges of Wyoming. These movements by mountain goats raised concerns about harmful effects to bighorn sheep and rare plants. Biologists expected mountain goats would reduce plant cover and increase bare areas in high mountain areas. They also thought mountain goats would compete with bighorn sheep for food and transmit respiratory diseases such as pneumonia to them.

To address these concerns, biologists from Montana State University compared vegetation conditions in areas with low and high use by mountain goats in Yellowstone National Park and nearby national forests during 2001 to 2009. Next, the National Park Service and Canon USA, Inc. provided funding to Montana State University to begin the Greater Yellowstone Area Mountain Ungulate Project. Many other agencies and organizations joined this effort with funding, resources, scholarships, and staff, including the Beaverhead and Bridger Teton national forests, Custer Gallatin National Forest, Grand Teton National Park, Idaho Fish and Game Department, International Order of Rocky Mountain Goats, Montana Department of Fish, Wildlife and Parks, Montana Wild Sheep Foundation, Shoshone National Forest, Targhee National Forest, Wyoming Governor's Big Game License Coalition, Wyoming Game and Fish Department, Wyoming Wild Sheep Foundation, and Yellowstone Forever.

Biologists conducted surveys and shared information to determine the numbers and distribution of bighorn sheep and mountain goats across the region. They evaluated the potential for competition between mountain goats and bighorn sheep for food and other resources. Biologists also documented the use of habitats and movements by bighorn sheep and mountain goats and monitored the survival of adults and young to understand population trends. In addition, they investigated the occurrence and effects of respiratory diseases. Biologists in Montana and Wyoming expanded these efforts during 2013 to 2019 to study more populations across a wider variety of areas in the region and elsewhere.

This book summarizes information on bighorn sheep and mountain goats in the Greater Yellowstone Area. The original sources of information are provided at the end of each paragraph so people can find additional details. Chapters 1 and 2 provide information on the behaviors, traits, and management history of bighorn sheep and mountain goats. Chapters 3 and 4 provide information on their habitat use and seasonal movements. Chapters 5 to 7 provide information on genetics, health and diseases, and population trends. Chapters 8 and 9 provide information on the potential impacts of mountain goat expansion and current management practices for bighorn sheep and mountain goats.

We hope this information will benefit wildlife professionals and students, as well as the millions of people that visit the area to observe wildlife or monitor their conservation and management via the Internet.

*Bighorn sheep ram. Photo by Mark Gocke.*

# Chapter 1
# Natural History:
# Life in the Mountains

*Andrew C. Pils and Kerry M. Murphy*

## BIGHORN SHEEP

Bighorn sheep in the Rocky Mountains, including the Greater Yellowstone Area, belong to the family *Bovidae*, which also includes bison (*Bison bison*) and cattle (*Bos taurus*), and the subfamily *Caprinae* that includes all wild sheep and goats. Bighorn sheep are large animals, with adult males (rams) weighing about 175 to 250 pounds (79 to 113 kilograms) and females (ewes) weighing about 130 to 190 pounds (59 to 86 kilograms). Bighorn sheep in the northern part of their range tend to weigh more than sheep in southerly areas. One of their most distinguishing characteristics is the large curled horns adult rams use for battling during the breeding season (rut). The hooves of bighorn sheep are blunt and widely cleaved, with hard edges to provide solid footing in rugged terrain. They are social animals, but usually live in smaller groups than bison, elk (*Cervus canadensis*), or pronghorn (*Antilocapra americana*). (Honess and Frost 1942, Valdez and Kraussman 1999)

## HISTORY

Bighorn sheep were widely distributed and abundant in many mountain ranges and badlands areas of the western United States prior to European settlement, extending north into Canada and south into Mexico. To the east, their range included what is now the western Dakotas and Nebraska, and to the west all but the coastal ranges and western slopes of the Sierra and Cascade mountains. There are no reliable estimates of their historic numbers, but some biologists have suggested up to two million. (Seton 1929, Buechner 1960)

Bighorn sheep were an important resource used for food and clothing by native people (see chapter 2). Hunters drove bighorn sheep into structures built to direct and entrap them or to waiting hunters. Bighorn sheep also had spiritual importance to native people. Early European explorers noted bighorn sheep skulls placed in trees in western Montana, where native people left offerings. (Frison 2004, Kornfeld et al. 2010)

Bighorn sheep numbers decreased following the westward expansion of European settlement. There were no regulations to limit harvests and the killing of animals for commercial sale was common. In addition, numbers of bighorn sheep decreased substantially after the introduction of livestock, particularly domestic sheep (*Ovis aries*), in the late 1800s. Some areas used by bighorn sheep were ideal for grazing domestic sheep, which competed with bighorn sheep for food and led to large die-offs by spreading diseases to them. (Honess and Frost 1942, Buechner 1960, Wild Sheep Working Group 2012)

In the late 1800s, Congress established the Forest Service and tasked it with managing grazing on national forest lands. Managers decreased numbers of domestic sheep on national forests after the world wars due to concerns about overgrazing. At the same time, public support for restoring wildlife populations throughout the western United States was building. The establishment of state and federal agencies charged with conserving wildlife, combined with the emerging science of wildlife biology, marked a turning point in the decline of many wildlife populations. Across the western United States, biologists began to re-establish many eliminated populations and increase remaining populations reduced in size by relocating animals from areas with larger remaining numbers. Today, domestic sheep numbers in the western United States are much lower than during the early 1900s. Biologists have restored bighorn sheep populations in many areas, though their numbers are still a fraction of what they once were. (Williams 2000, Picton and Lonner 2008, Wild Sheep Working Group 2014, 2015)

## HABITAT AND DIET

The defining feature of bighorn sheep habitat is closeness to rugged, steep terrain where they can escape from predators (see chapter 3). Cliffs, rim rocks, and ledges are commonly used for bedding and resting. Bighorn sheep usually feed on slopes, ridgelines, and mesa tops near escape terrain, and quickly move there if threatened. Few other animals have similar mobility in such terrain. Bighorn sheep sometimes use relatively flat land further from escape terrain, usually high-quality feeding areas. Another common characteristic of bighorn sheep habitat is open country with long views of the surrounding area so they can see predators from a distance. Bighorn sheep generally avoid areas with tall vegetation that blocks their view. However, they will use patches of forest for shelter from inclement weather or heat and when moving between seasonal ranges. (Honess and Frost 1942, Valdez and Kraussman 1999)

Bighorn sheep in the Rocky Mountains often move among seasonal habitats (see chapter 4). Long-distance migrations still occur in some populations, but most make shorter movements between seasonal ranges. Alpine or subalpine areas in the mountains provide classic summer ranges for bighorn sheep, where the vegetation is typically grasses, sedges, and forbs. In some cases, bighorn sheep spend winter in high-elevation, wind-blown areas near their summer ranges. However, many animals move to lower elevation valleys or foothills where snow is shallower during the winter. Vegetation in such areas is typically a mixture of grasses, forbs, and shrubs. In some places, bighorn sheep live in low-elevation areas year-round, demonstrating they are adapted to using a wide variety of habitats from the highest mountains to low-elevation deserts. (Honess and Frost 1942, Buechner 1960)

*Classic bighorn sheep habitat with rugged, steep terrain to escape predators, cliffs and ledges commonly used for bedding and resting, and open slopes near steep terrain for foraging. This image is from the Absaroka Range. Photo by Doug McWhirter, Wyoming Game and Fish Department.*

Bighorn sheep live in a wide variety of habitats and, therefore, have broad and varied diets of grasses, forbs, and shrubs. A study of one herd in Wyoming found they consumed 37 different plants. Bighorn sheep generally prefer eating grasses and forbs, but diets vary based on age, sex, and seasonal plant availability and growth. (Honess and Frost 1942, Laundré 1994, Valdez and Kraussman 1999)

## Diseases and Parasites

Bighorn sheep are subject to a variety of diseases (see chapter 6). The most significant of these is pneumonia, a respiratory disease that can cause large die-offs of adults and young animals and result in few lambs surviving to adulthood for many years. Although our understanding of the disease has improved considerably in recent years, there is still much uncertainty and debate about its causes. Most biologists think several species of bacteria usually contribute to outbreaks of pneumonia in bighorn sheep. The primary bacteria causing pneumonia are from the family Pasteurellaceae (*Pasteurella multocida*, *Mannheimia haemolytica*, and *Bibersteinia trehalosi*) and *Mycoplasma ovipneumoniae*. Of these, *Mycoplasma ovipneumoniae* may be the most important because it predisposes bighorn sheep to infection by other disease-causing organisms. (Besser et al. 2013, Cassirer et al. 2017a, Butler et al. 2018)

Domestic sheep carry bacteria involved with pneumonia and can transmit them to bighorn sheep. Studies with captive animals have shown that fatal pneumonia often develops in bighorn sheep following contact with domestic sheep. However, contact with domestic sheep is not always responsible for pneumonia outbreaks in bighorn sheep. Domestic goats (*Capra aegagrus hircus*) also carry and can transmit the bacteria to bighorn sheep. In addition, bighorn sheep can carry and transmit the bacteria among themselves. Furthermore, each type of bacteria may have different strains, with some being more infectious than others. The introduction of new bacterial strains to a population after contact with domestic sheep or goats, or other bighorn sheep, may result in the development of pneumonia. Factors such as severe weather, malnutrition, and concentrations of animals in an area may trigger pneumonia outbreaks in populations that have carried a variety of diseases for years without experiencing outbreaks previously. (Besser et al. 2012a,b, 2017; Cassirer et al. 2017a, b; Butler et al. 2018)

Bighorn sheep are subject to other diseases less lethal than pneumonia that, as a result, have fewer effects on population trends. Bighorn sheep can contract infectious keratoconjunctivitis, also known as pinkeye, which is a highly contagious bacterial eye infection common in domestic sheep and goats. Infection causes redness of the eyes, blinking, discharge, and, in some cases, blindness and accidental death. In addition, bighorn sheep can develop contagious ecthyma, also called sore mouth or orf, which is a viral disease common in domestic sheep, goats, and llamas (*Lama glama*). Sores usually form on the lips and muzzle of infected animals, but occasionally on the udder, feet, or vulva. Sore mouth can be very painful, interfering with chewing and resulting in a loss of body weight (mass). The disease is typically not lethal, though it can cause death in animals with numerous parasites, bacterial infections, or poor nutritional condition. (Samuel et al. 1975, Janovsky et al. 2001, Whithear 2001, Giacometti et al. 2002)

Bighorn sheep are also carriers of parasites, including the lungworm *Protostrongylus* that occurs only in bighorn sheep and *Muellerius capillaris*, which is a common lungworm of domestic sheep and goats. Some biologists believe lungworm infection can predispose bighorn sheep to pneumonia, but the bulk of the evidence indicates lungworms are not an important factor. Psoroptic scabies is a condition resulting from infestation by a parasitic skin mite. The original source of scabies in bighorn sheep is unknown, although it most likely occurred from contact with domestic sheep. It is now widespread in bighorn sheep in the Rocky Mountains. Infestations are usually mild and most often affect the ears, although in severe cases it can affect the entire body. People thought many large bighorn sheep die-offs in the late 1800s and early 1900s were due to scabies, though it now seems more likely pneumonia caused these events. (Honess and Frost 1942, Buechner 1960, Forrester 1971, Bunch et al. 1999, Foreyt et al. 2009, Ezenwa et al. 2010, Wild Sheep Working Group 2012, Cassirer et al. 2017a)

## POPULATION DYNAMICS

Numbers of bighorn sheep usually increase slowly when nutrition is good, and survival is high. Pregnancy rates in most populations are high because one ram can breed several ewes. Most ewes have their first lambs when they are three years old, although in populations with good nutrition many females may give birth when they are two. Ewes typically have one lamb, and twins are rare. The lambing season for bighorn sheep in the Rocky Mountains is generally from late May through June. (Honess and Frost 1942, Buechner 1960)

A variety of factors influence the population trends of bighorn sheep (see chapters 5 through 7). Pneumonia is the main factor because outbreaks can lead to large die-offs affecting all ages and both sexes. Very often, lamb deaths due to pneumonia continue for years after an outbreak that causes a die-off across all ages. Large decreases in bighorn sheep numbers prolong the time necessary for a population to recover or prevent recovery altogether. In addition, the number of bighorn sheep living in an area, called density, can affect nutrition and, indirectly, have a strong effect on population trends. When the density of bighorn sheep is high, the availability of nutritious food for each animal typically declines, especially for young animals such as lambs. As a result, their survival often decreases. Environmental conditions may also affect nutrition. Low spring precipitation and deep snow during winter can both limit food availability, resulting in lower lamb survival. (Portier et al. 1998, Besser et al. 2013, Cassirer et al. 2013)

Living in the rugged environments generally protects bighorn sheep from most predators and, as a result, predation usually has little influence on population trends. Wolves (*Canis lupus*) and grizzly bears (*Ursus arctos*) are occasional predators of bighorn sheep in the Yellowstone area, and coyotes (*Canis latrans*) and golden eagles (*Aquila chrysaetos*) may prey on lambs they encounter. Cougars (mountain lions, *Puma concolor*) can effectively prey on bighorn sheep and, in some cases, have significantly affected population trends. Such situations may be more likely when there is little escape terrain or vegetation restricts visibility. (Buechner 1960, Geist 1971, Sawyer and Lindzey 2002, Metz et al. 2012)

## MANAGEMENT

Bighorn sheep are a highly charismatic species greatly valued by wildlife enthusiasts including hunters, wildlife watchers, and photographers. They require special management because of the disease issues discussed previously and smaller population sizes compared to ungulates such as elk or deer (see chapters 5 and 6). Outside national parks, state, tribal, and provincial wildlife agencies manage bighorn sheep as game animals where populations are large enough to sustain harvests. Biologists typically design hunting seasons to allow the harvest of a limited number of rams to provide recreational hunting opportunities, rather than to reduce population size. (Wild Sheep Working Group 2014)

Relocation, also known as translocation, has been a primary method used for the restoration of bighorn sheep and continues to be an important tool used for re-establishing eliminated herds or augmenting existing ones. However, translocation can be risky because relocated bighorn sheep could inadvertently carry new diseases or strains and infect sheep in the target population. (Wild Sheep Working Group 2015, Cassirer et al. 2017a, Butler et al. 2018)

Reducing the risk of pneumonia-related die-offs is a major focus of bighorn sheep management by wildlife agencies. Current recommendations are to maintain separation between domestic sheep or goats and bighorn sheep. Land management agencies may consider the potential for contact between domestic and bighorn sheep when deciding whether to issue permits for grazing domestic sheep on public lands.

*The Greater Yellowstone Area has a full complement of predators capable of preying on bighorn sheep and mountain goats. These include (clockwise from upper left) mountain lions, golden eagles, wolves, and grizzly bears. Coyotes, black bears, and even a few wolverines call the Greater Yellowstone Area home as well. Photos by National Park Service employees Dan Stahler (upper left), Neal Herbert (upper right), Jacob Frank (lower right), and Jim Peaco (lower left).*

These processes have resulted in a variety of outcomes, including halting domestic sheep grazing in some areas, switching to other types of livestock that do not pose a disease risk to bighorn sheep, or permitting domestic sheep grazing while implementing measures to reduce the risk of contact with bighorn sheep. Voluntary buyouts of grazing permits brokered by bighorn sheep advocacy groups also have been used to reduce the potential for contact between domestic and bighorn sheep. Biologists sometimes lethally remove bighorn sheep that move outside their normal ranges and encounter domestic sheep or goats to prevent them from infecting other bighorn sheep. (Wild Sheep Working Group 2012, Cassirer et al. 2017a)

Biologists have explored other tools for reducing the risk of disease-related die-offs, with mixed results. Because populations with higher densities of bighorn sheep may be at increased risk of disease-related die-offs, biologists have relocated animals from some larger populations to reduce densities. Harvests, particularly of reproductive-age females, are also an option for reducing population density. Some biologists have proposed managing for larger, well-distributed, but interconnected, populations to increase resistance to, and recovery from, disease outbreaks. (Buechner 1960, Wild Sheep Working Group 2014, Cassirer et al. 2017a)

To date, efforts to manage pneumonia outbreaks after they are in progress by culling, or killing, bighorn sheep with signs of the disease have been met with variable results. In some cases, biologists have killed bighorn sheep surviving large die-offs because the survivors still carried pneumonia-causing bacteria. Biologists then restored the populations using bighorn sheep relocated from other populations. Existing antibiotics or vaccines have not been effective tools for managing pneumonia. (Cassirer et al. 2017a, Wood et al. 2017)

## MOUNTAIN GOATS

Mountain goats are hooved animals in the *Bovidae* family, belonging to the subfamily *Caprinae* (goat) and the tribe *Rupicaprini*. They are skilled mountain climbers with stocky bodies, slender necks, short legs, dagger-like horns, and white or yellowish-white fur that blends in with snow. They are about 3 feet (1 meter) tall and 4 feet (1.2 meters) long. Adult males are about 40 percent heavier than females. Mid-summer weights of males range from about 190 to 245 pounds (86 to 111 kilograms), while female weights range from about 120 to 160 pounds (56 to 73 kilograms). (Chadwick 1983, Côté and Festa-Bianchet 2001, 2003)

*A mountain goat demonstrating the affinity of this species for rock-dominated habitats. Photo by Mark Gocke.*

Mountain goats have several traits that suit them for mountain living, communicating with other herd members, and self-defense. Their forequarters are well-muscled for up-hill climbing in steep terrain. The winter coat consists of long guard hairs and a thick under layer of wool that withstands cold temperatures and wind. They have broad, oval-shaped hooves that splay to increase traction when descending steep slopes and are useful for pawing through crusted snow. Their long, sharp horns are used to communicate threats to other mountain goats and defend against attacking predators. Dermal shields, which are areas of thick skin on their rump, protect them from horn punctures during confrontations with other goats. (Geist 1964, 1967; Holroyd 1967, Wigal and Coggins 1982)

During summer, mountain goats separate into bachelor groups of one or more males and nursery groups of adult females and their kids, yearlings, and 2-year-olds of both sexes. Males move from nursery groups to bachelor groups at 3 to 4 years of age. Adult males are less social and do not mingle with nursery groups outside the breeding season, or rut, which occurs from late October through mid-November. Mountain goats have a mating system in which dominant males defend a group of females from other adult males and breed as many females as possible. (Chadwick 1983)

## History

Mountain goats are native to the coastal and inland mountain ranges west of the continental divide in North America. Native populations extend along the Pacific coast from southeastern Alaska to southcentral Washington, and southerly in the Rocky Mountains into central Idaho and western Montana. These regions are relatively cool and moist, with a climatic zone strongly influenced by the Pacific Ocean. The largest native populations occur in southern Alaska and British Columbia. To increase hunting opportunities, mountain goats were reintroduced within their native range in Alaska, Idaho, Montana, Washington, and southern Alberta. (Johnson 1977, Côté and Festa-Bianchet 2003, Flesch et al. 2016)

Many state wildlife agencies in the western United States also transplanted mountain goats into historically unoccupied habitat during the mid-1900s (see chapter 2). Many introduced populations became well established, showing high rates of growth. Collectively, the translocation programs were largely successful in expanding the species' range. Continentally, native and introduced mountain goats number about 75,000 to 110,000 individuals. (Johnson 1977, Côté and Festa-Bianchet 2003)

Indigenous people did not heavily exploit mountain goats owing to the species' affinity for rugged and remote terrain and harsh environmental conditions. However, they were a source of food, utensils, weapons (horn sheaths), breast armor (thick hides), and blankets (wooly underfur). In contrast to most large mammals in North America, mountain goat numbers and range were not greatly reduced during early European settlement due to the inaccessibility of the species. Restrictions on mountain goat hunting occurred at the beginning of the 20th century, like protections for other North American big game. (Cahalane 1947, Wigal and Coggins 1982, Chadwick 1983)

## HABITAT AND DIET

In nearly all their geographic range, mountain goats inhabit the subalpine and alpine zone, using habitat types from tree line to nearby ridges and peaks. In coastal Alaska and British Columbia, they also occupy heavily forested areas at low elevations with interspersed steep, rocky terrain. They occupy the extreme end of the continuum for terrain ruggedness, harsh weather, and snow and consistently use steep slopes and cliffs that provide sites for foraging, cover from weather, and security from predators. They are habitat specialists, able to use their unique adaptations to occupy areas largely unexploited by other ungulates. (Adams and Bailey 1982, Chadwick 1983)

Mountain goat habitat is naturally patchy due to the limited distribution of steep, rocky terrain in mountainous environments (see chapter 3). Snow cover persists for 8

*Mountain goat habitat in the Beartooth Mountains along the Montana–Wyoming border. Mountain goats make use of cliffs in and below the trees as well as cliffs well above the trees. The key words are steep and rugged. Photo by Shawn T. Stewart.*

to 9 months of the year, often restricting access to forage. Weather is harsh, with high winds, low average daily temperatures, and heavy winter snowfall. For some populations, natural salt licks are important seasonal resources visited after travelling long distances to compensate for sodium deficiency. Together with food sources, these habitat features largely dictate mountain goat movements and local distribution. Mountain goats typically avoid subalpine forests with high canopy cover, although in coastal regions they often use low-elevation forests with heavy canopies that shield snow from the ground. The availability of open water seldom limits mountain goat movements or distribution, as water is available directly from snowbanks, seepage springs, or rivulets. (Brandborg 1955, Holroyd 1967, Hebert and Cowan 1971, Singer and Dougherty 1985, Hopkins et al. 1992, Poole et al. 2009)

The winter season is challenging for mountain goats due to the increased energetic costs of thermoregulation, travel, and foraging. Mountain goats use steep slopes, middle or low elevations, and southerly aspects to minimize energy costs. Snow on these sites is shallower than at high elevations, temperatures are higher, and solar radiation reduces the snowpack. Mountain goats also use wind-swept ridges at high elevations to access forage. (Poole et al. 2009)

Mountain goats have only 3 to 4 months during late spring, summer, and early fall to accumulate metabolic reserves required for survival, growth, and reproduction. The timing of vegetation green-up has a strong influence on growth of young goats and the physical condition of prime-age females. Adult females in Alberta are known to increase their weight by 38 percent during the summer, bolstered by abundant, nutritious forage. During this time, they follow the upward progression of snow melt and greening vegetation to rugged alpine areas, foraging in open areas in or near steep, rugged terrain, but avoiding sites with direct exposure to the hot summer sun. (Varley 1994, Festa-Bianchet and Côté 2008)

Mountain goats are generalist herbivores (plant eaters) whose diets vary by season across their geographic range and even among different individuals that live in the same area. Diets are typically dominated by grasses, with alpine forbs increasing in importance during the spring and summer. Their summer diet, summarized across 10 studies, averaged 56 percent grasses, 30 percent forbs, and 16 percent browse. Winter diets averaged 60 percent grasses, 8 percent forbs, and 32 percent browse. The fraction of browse, including twigs and needles of subalpine conifers, may increase in winter because they are often above the snowline compared to grasses and sedges that are commonly buried. Shrubs also contain higher levels of protein than other winter forage. (Hebert and Turnbull 1977, Chadwick 1983, Laundré 1994, Côté and Festa-Bianchet 2003)

## DISEASES AND PARASITES

Little research is available concerning the diseases and parasites of mountain goats. The relationship between these mortality factors and the mountain goat population dynamics is poorly understood (see chapter 6). Some diseases that are potentially important stressors in mountain goat populations may have originally resulted from exposure to domestic livestock. Mountain goats are also carriers of types of bacteria that can cause pneumonia in bighorn sheep. Biologists detected *Mycoplasma ovipneumoniae*, thought to play an important role in facilitating the development of pneumonia in bighorn sheep, in mountain goats in Nevada and the Greater Yellowstone Area. About 10 to 20 percent of two mountain goat herds in Nevada succumbed to pneumonia during 2009 and 2010. The herds also likely transmitted bacteria to bighorn sheep on shared ranges, leading to a catastrophic die-off for the latter species as well. Bacteria of the family Pasteurellaceae (*Pasteurella multocida*, *Mannheimia haemolytica*, or *Bibersteinia trehalosi*) have also been detected in mountain goats from different geographic regions. More research is needed to better understand the dynamics of pneumonia in mountain goat populations, including the potential for disease transmission between mountain goats and bighorn sheep. (Toweill et al. 2004, Wolff et al. 2014, 2016; Lowrey et al. 2018a)

Other diseases have been documented in mountain goats, including contagious ecthyma (sore mouth), paratuberculosis (Johne's disease), and several different viral infections. The species also is known to harbor a variety of skin and internal parasites. The most serious of these is probably lungworms of the genus *Protostrongylus*, which contribute to poor body condition and  death in some cases. (Samuel et al. 1975, Dunbar et al. 1986, Toweill et al. 2004, Wolff et al. 2014)

## POPULATION DYNAMICS

The greatest limiting factor for mountain goat populations is extreme weather, a potent force that mediates access to forage during winter and early spring (see chapter 7). Heavy snowpack and crusted snow concentrates animals on limited winter range where forage becomes increasingly depleted, increasing the susceptibility of animals to starvation, malnutrition, and other mortality factors. Most deaths occur during the winter and are associated with the loss of body condition among old and young animals. Kids and yearlings, characterized by slower growth rates than young of other North American ungulates, are disadvantaged by their small relative size, low fat reserves, labored travel and foraging in deep snow, and low social rank at foraging sites. The mortality of kids and yearlings are elevated in severe winters. Biologists documented population declines of 82 and 92 percent in two populations in British Columbia following a severe winter. Because winter severity affects the body condition of adult females (which determines the birth weight of the kids) and their ability to produce milk, it also influences the number and survival of newborns. (Rideout 1974, Adams and Bailey 1982, Hebert and Langin 1982, Wigal and Coggins 1982, Chadwick 1983)

Harsh conditions in mountain goat habitat have a strong effect on population growth, including how populations respond after declines. Mountain goats produce their first young when they are 3 or 4 years old. Therefore, fewer mountain goats (50 to 60 percent) produce young than females of most other ungulates (75 percent).

Twinning is uncommon in mountain goat populations that are near carrying capacity. A low female reproductive rate combined with high over-winter mortality of young leads to slow population growth. For these reasons, many mountain goat populations exhibit little or no density-related increases in reproduction and survival following declines, as is commonly observed among other ungulates. (Chadwick 1983, Toweill et al. 2004)

In contrast, many introduced herds initially show high rates of kid production, including frequent twinning, and exhibit rapid population growth. This is due to a variety of factors including limited competition for forage, few predators, alpine plants lacking natural defenses to herbivory, and mild climates that support strong plant production. For example, an introduced population in Idaho exhibited a 22% annual increase over 12 years. (Hayden 1984)

Mountain goats die due to a variety of causes, including accidental falls, avalanches, predators, diseases, and parasites. Mortality from these factors is predisposed by severe winters. Use of steep terrain during the winter exposes mountain goats to avalanches. Because mountain goats communicate through threat displays and avoid physical aggression in interactions with other band members, lethal injuries due to intraspecific strife are uncommon. (Geist 1964, Chadwick 1983)

Cougars, grizzly bears, and wolves are occasional predators of mountain goats, along with wolverines (*Gulo gulo*), eagles, and coyotes. However, predation is not considered a significant source of mortality for the species. Predators such as wolves that capture prey through pursuit caused extensive use of escape habitat to be favored in the mountain goat's evolution. Likewise, ambush predators such as cougars and bears incur significant risk of injury when hunting mountain goats in steep terrain. For this reason, most kills by large predators occur outside escape terrain. (Chadwick 1983, Festa-Bianchet and Côté 2008)

*A mountain goat hunter peers over the edge of the Clarks Fork Canyon in Wyoming. In some situations, mountain goats can be sensitive to overharvest, with introduced populations less vulnerable. Photo by Doug McWhirter, Wyoming Game and Fish Department.*

## MANAGEMENT

Mountain goats are highly valued by hunters, and most states and provinces manage them as trophy big game (see chapter 9). Hunting licenses are offered on a quota system to limit harvests to sustainable levels. Owing to their low rate of reproduction and high annual mortality, mountain goat populations are sensitive to overharvest. Hunting mortality appears to be additive to other sources of mortality. Small and highly accessible populations may be at risk of extirpation when management includes sport hunting. Lacking adequate survey information and a poor understanding of the species' population dynamics, early managers set hunting quotas based on assumptions and game management principles they applied to other North American ungulates. As a result, several native herds were severely reduced or extirpated during the 1970s and 1980s due to over-harvest. Bolstered by research studies and better survey information, managers now apply more conservative hunting regulations. Introduced populations in early stages of population growth can withstand higher rates of hunting mortality due to higher reproductive and survival rates. (Kuck 1977, Hebert 1978, Glasgow et al. 2003, Toweill et al. 2004, Festa-Bianchet and Côté 2008)

During the 1970s and 1980s, human disturbance in mountain goat habitat from energy exploration, timber sales, and recreation increased significantly. These activities introduced new stressors to which the species was unaccustomed, and triggered declines of several native populations. These disturbances were likely interactive with natural sources of mortality, and further reduced the resilience of populations. (Wigal and Coggins 1982, Joslin 1986)

## CONCLUSIONS

In contrast to many native herds, some introduced mountain goat populations increased in size and distribution to the extent that managers became concerned about their effects on other resources. Although charismatic and popular with the public, mountain goats may damage soils and graze fragile alpine flora that did not evolve with herbivory. They also may compete for forage or habitat with bighorn sheep, and the transfer of diseases may occur where the two species use the same habitat at the same time (see chapter 8). In Olympic National Park, mountain goats introduced during the 1920s caused damage to soils and vegetation. However, the effects of introduced populations on habitat, and agency management of the species, differs among jurisdictions. The remaining chapters in this book provide information gleaned from management activities and research regarding these and other topics. (Chadwick 1983, Houston and Schreiner 1995, Schullery and Whittlesey 2001, Lemke 2004, Festa-Bianchet and Côté 2008)

*A small ewe/lamb group on alpine summer range typical of the Absaroka Mountains. Photo by Joe Riis.*

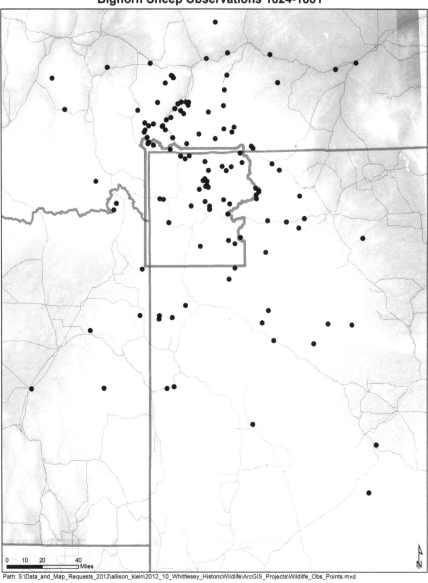

Path: S:\Data_and_Map_Requests_2012\allison_klein\2012_10_Whittlesey_HistoricWildlife\ArcGIS_Projects\Wildlife_Obs_Points.mxd

*Figure 1. Observations of bighorn sheep in the Greater Yellowstone Area during 1824 to 1881 (Whittlesey et al. 2018, Whittlesey and Bone 2020). The green outline depicts Yellowstone National Park, established in 1872, while the gray lines are the boundaries of Idaho, Montana, and Wyoming, established during 1889 and 1890. Map by Allison Klein, National Park Service.*

# Chapter 2
# Historic Information

*P. J. White, Douglas E. McWhirter, Robert A. Garrott, and Daniel B. Tyers*

## ORIGINAL DISTRIBUTION

There are estimates of up to two million bighorn sheep west of the Mississippi River from the Dakotas to the Pacific and from Canada to Mexico before settlement by mainly European immigrants. They were widespread and plentiful in parts of the Greater Yellowstone Area (Figure 1). During 1865 to 1881, travelers reported many bighorn sheep within Yellowstone National Park and north in Montana along Bear Creek, in the Gallatin Mountains, and in the Paradise Valley. They also saw many bighorn sheep east in the Clark's Fork area, Absaroka Mountains, and the Wind River Mountains of Wyoming. In addition, travelers observed many bighorn sheep west along the Madison River and near Henry's Lake in Montana and Idaho, as well as south in the Teton Range of Wyoming. (Seton 1929, Buechner 1960, Whittlesey et al. 2018, Whittlesey and Bone 2020)

Mountain goats ranged from southern Alaska through the Northwest and Yukon territories, south into British Columbia and western Alberta in Canada, and into the northwestern portion of the United States (Washington, Oregon, and western Idaho and Montana). Fossils of mountain goats from about 70,000 years ago were discovered near the Palisades Reservoir in Idaho in the southeastern portion of the Greater Yellowstone Area. In addition, fossils indicate mountain goats lived in portions of western Wyoming 10,000 to 15,000 years ago. However, only a few written accounts mention mountain goats in the Greater Yellowstone Area during the 1800s. There was a report of an Army hunting party killing a mountain goat in the southern Teton Range of Wyoming during the 1840s. Also, prospectors reported a "Rocky mountain goat" in the Gallatin Mountain Range south of Emigrant, Montana during September 1864; however, other accounts by people familiar with the area suggest the animal was more likely a light-colored bighorn sheep with small horns. A visiting European hunter reported finding a spearhead or scraper near Big Creek, Montana in 1874, which he speculated an Indian might have dropped while hunting "goats and sheep." In 1871, a photographer listed animals, including "mountain sheep, goat or ibex," supposedly located within 5 miles (8 kilometers) of the Mud Volcano area in central Yellowstone. However, neither the hunter nor the photographer said they observed mountain goats in those areas. In addition, an 1883 ban on hunting in Yellowstone National Park issued from Washington, D.C. listed several game species, including "Rocky mountain goat." However, the accuracy of this list is doubtful because it included several species not found in the park such as prairie chicken (*Tympanuchus cupido*), pheasant (*Phasianus colchicus*), partridge (*Alectoris chukar, Perdix perdix*), and quail (*Oreortyx pictus*). Overall, the lack of dependable observations in the Greater Yellowstone Area during the 1800s suggests mountain goats were absent or rare. (Cooke 1847-1848, Dunraven 1876:351, Calfee 1899, Vaughan 1900:35-36, Skinner 1926, Laundré 1990, Schullery and Whittlesey 2001, Côté and Festa-Bianchet 2003, McWhirter 2004, Whittlesey et al. 2018, Whittlesey and Bone 2020)

## INFLUENCE OF NATIVE PEOPLE

Several tribes have lived in the Greater Yellowstone Area for more than 10,000 years, including the Bannock, Blackfeet, Crow, Kootenai, Nez Perce, Salish, and Shoshone. These tribes brought a variety of cultures to the region, including knowledge and traditions from the Great Plains to the east, the Plateau (or Salmon) area to the northwest, the Great Basin to the southwest, and the Rocky Mountains to the north and south. Prior to Euro-American settlement, native people lived as part of the natural community with sustainable fishing, hunting, and gathering practices. Other activities included collecting obsidian rocks for arrow and spear points, creating rock art sites, conducting ceremonies and councils, and trading goods such as bows, clothing, food, hides, and obsidian. At times, they lit fires to remove brush, clear downed timber, move game animals, and replenish food and medicinal plants. (Nabokov and Loendorf 2004, Confederated Salish and Kootenai Tribes 2005)

Members of some tribes moved through the Greater Yellowstone Area seasonally, while others lived year-round in the mountains and valleys. For example, the upper Snake River and Lemhi River valley bands of the Shoshone and Bannock tribes traveled through the area on horseback to buffalo hunting areas, while hunting, fishing, and gathering berries and plants along the way. Other bands of Shoshone, called Sheep Eaters, lived year-round in the area, following bighorn sheep as they moved seasonally. Some Sheep Eaters lived in wickiups made of timber poles propped into a tepee shape and covered by tanned hides. Others lived in rock shelters or caves with timber poles interwoven with brush covering the openings or log structures made of stacked deadfall timber. They used pack dogs (*Canis lupus familiaris*) to transport materials and hunted bighorn sheep, deer (*Odocoileus hemionus*), elk, and small game. In addition, they fished with lines, dams, and traps, while drying berries, fish, meat, and roots to eat or trade later. (Nabokov and Loendorf 2004, Historical Research Associates 2006a,b,c; Lewis 2008, Mistretta 2012)

Bighorn sheep were a staple resource for food, clothing, glue, and tools for native people in the Greater Yellowstone Area, especially the Sheep Eaters and a part of the Crow tribe called "Those Who Eat Bighorn Sheep" who lived near Cedar Mountain and the Shoshone River in Wyoming. Some hunters drove bighorn sheep into deep snow where they were less mobile and easier to harvest or towards pits with hidden hunters. Others developed traps, blinds, fences, and jumps for harvesting bighorn sheep, bison, deer, and elk. Hunters positioned traps and fences made of rocks and deadfall timber in funnel or hook shapes, with wings leading to catch pens made of logs or natural features such as rock walls. Sheep Eaters built short bows from bighorn sheep horns by softening them in hot water or heating them in coals, cutting a strip from each horn, and straightening and shaping the strips. Hunters strengthened the spliced joint (grip) between the two strips with another piece of horn held in place by sinew or rawhide and glue. These bows had pull strengths of 60 to 70 pounds and could kill large animals using arrows with wooden shafts and obsidian points. Native people also used horns and bones from bighorn sheep to make tools, such as for chipping and shaping obsidian rocks. (Holm 1982, Nabokov and Loendorf 2004 and references therein, Eakin 2005)

## EFFECTS OF EURO-AMERICAN SETTLEMENT

Settlements were scarce and isolated in the American west through the 1840s, and livestock were uncommon. However, the discovery of gold in California in 1848 led to a large movement of settlers into the west. During 1849 to 1851, for example, about 150,000 people and 100,000 livestock moved through passes in the Rocky Mountains located south of the Wind River Range. Later gold strikes in the northern portion of the Greater Yellowstone Area led to the arrival of many more prospectors and settlers during the 1860s and 1870s. Thousands of these settlers traveled in wagons along the Bozeman Trail, which was located east of the Greater Yellowstone Area and skirted the Bighorn Mountains in Wyoming. These settlers removed vegetation to build settlements and grow crops. They also killed predators to protect themselves and their livestock. (Buechner 1960, Edgar and Turnell 1979, Gill 2010)

Settlement of farmable lands in the Yellowstone region increased during the 1870s and 1880s following the 1862 Homestead Act, which granted 160 acres free to each settler who "improved" the land for 5 years. Some of these settlers brought domestic cattle and sheep for ranching. Sheep were often preferred because there

*Remnants of a rock fence associated with a bighorn sheep trap in the Absaroka Range. These fences often led to a cliff and associated catch-pen. Bighorn sheep were very important for food, clothing, utensils, and weapons to the Mountain Shoshone or Sheep Eater Indians. Photo by Doug McWhirter, Wyoming Game and Fish Department.*

were few fences and herders with dogs could control and move them between seasonal ranges. Moreover, settlers of the western frontier were often from cultures accustomed to managing sheep. For example, many settlers in the northern part of the Greater Yellowstone Area were shepherds from Norway. (Smith 2002, Pioneer Society of Sweet Grass County 2008, Stryker 2009, Hooker 2011)

Market hunters slaughtered bighorn sheep and other large animals in the Greater Yellowstone Area during the mid- to late-1800s. One writer reported a string of wagons loaded with hides from bighorn sheep, bison, deer, and elk traveling through the Paradise Valley north of Yellowstone National Park to Bozeman, Montana in 1872. The Superintendent of Yellowstone National Park reported poachers had taken nearly 2,000 hides of bighorn sheep out of the park during the spring of 1875. Another writer reported one fur trading company in Bozeman shipped 960 pounds (435 kilograms) of bighorn sheep hides during October 1881 to July 1882. Traders hauled many of these hides north to Fort Benton on the Missouri River for shipments east. To illustrate the number of wildlife killed in the region during the 1870s to mid-1880s, a single trader in Fort Benton bought 12,450 bison robes, 68,780 pounds (31,198 kilograms) of deer, elk, pronghorn, and beaver (*Castor canadensis*) hides; and 11,090 hides total from badgers (*Taxidea taxus*), bears, coyotes, fishers (*Martes pennanti*), foxes (*Vulpes vulpes*), lynx (*Lynx canadensis*), martin (*Martes americana*), mink (*Neovison vison*), muskrats (*Ondatra zibethicus*), wolverines, and wolves during 1875. (N.V.S. 1872, Avant Courier 1875, Norris 1878, Angler 1883, Whittlesey et al. 2018, Whittlesey and Bone 2020)

By the 1870s, most tribes in the Greater Yellowstone Area were struggling to persist following the settlement of their lands, outbreaks of diseases brought by settlers, and the slaughter of wildlife. Treaties with the federal government restricted their movements and use of traditional lands for hunting and gathering, including in Yellowstone National Park. Instead, federal agents confined them to reservations where many depended on government rations for survival. For example, by 1880 the upper Snake River and Lemhi River valley bands were supposed to stay on the Fort Hall and Lemhi reservations in Idaho territory, while federal agents moved the Sheep Eater bands living inside Yellowstone National Park to reservations in the Idaho and Wyoming territories. In addition, settlers and park managers suppressed fires in lower elevation areas and, as a result, conifers invaded many grassland habitats used by bighorn sheep. (Harris 1889, Meagher and Houston 1998, Nabokov and Loendorf 2004, Confederated Salish and Kootenai Tribes 2005, Historical Research Associates 2006a,b,c)

Ranchers brought cattle into the Greater Yellowstone Area by 1867, with numerous ranches established through the 1870s. In addition, Congress passed the 1862 Pacific Railway Act to provide the land needed to build railroad lines across the country. The Union Pacific railroad reached the Yellowstone River in 1871 and the Northern Pacific completed a branch line to near the northern boundary of Yellowstone National Park in 1883. These and other railroad lines encouraged settlement and led to a rapid increase in livestock in the region by providing a means for exporting them to national and international markets. There were 35 to 40 million cattle in western states by the mid-1880s, and ranchers brought large numbers of domestic sheep into the Wyoming Territory and the Yellowstone region from Oregon. In 1881, there were less than 30,000 domestic sheep in the Yellowstone region; by 1894, there were more than 500,000. There were 5 million domestic sheep in Montana and Wyoming by the 1920s and close to 10 million in the Greater Yellowstone Area by the 1930s and 1940s. (Rush 1933, Gill 2010, Tyers et al. 2017, U.S. Department of Agriculture 2017)

Some ranchers grazed cattle, horses (*Equus ferus caballus*), and domestic sheep within the northern portion of Yellowstone National Park from about 1875 to 1922, without any limits on numbers or season of use. In addition, in 1877 the Yellowstone Park Association brought 91 cattle and 300 domestic sheep into the park to graze and provide food and milk for visitors. The park issued similar permits each year until 1905 for businesses to graze livestock in the Canyon, Lake, Mammoth, Old Faithful, and West Thumb areas. (Whittlesey 1994, Meagher and Houston 1998)

A distinctive lifestyle developed in the Greater Yellowstone Area, with shepherds moving large bands of domestic sheep from winter ranges on the prairie to summer ranges in the mountains (Figure 2). By the late 1800s, the town of Big Timber, Montana, in the northern portion of the area, was the unofficial sheep capitol of the United States. Merchants shipped more wool from Big Timber than from anywhere else in the country during that period. Winter range for domestic sheep was plentiful on nearby prairies, the railroad provided access to markets, and public land for summer pasture was available in the nearby Absaroka, Beartooth, and Crazy mountains. Similarly, by the 1920s, shepherds were grazing about 325,000 domestic sheep during summer in the Wind River Mountains in the southern portion of the area. Bighorn sheep resided in all these summer ranges. (Rush 1933, Buechner 1960, Hawkes 1976, Smith 1982, Hurley and Firchow 1994, Ryder and Lanka 1997, Smith 2002, Nabokov and Loendorf 2004, Historical Research Associates 2006a, Picton and Lonner 2008, Pioneer Society of Sweet Grass County 2008, Stryker 2009, Gill 2010, Hooker 2011, Tyers et al. 2017, U.S. Department of Agriculture 2017)

The need for wool products during the two world wars kept the domestic sheep industry thriving in the Yellowstone region until the 1950s. Ranchers expanded grazing into nearly all drainages and higher-elevation pastures in the area. With such large numbers of widely distributed domestic sheep, the Forest Service became concerned about overgrazing, soil erosion, and the displacement of wildlife. In addition, diseases spread by livestock killed many bighorn sheep, including in the Absaroka and Wind River mountains in the eastern portion of the Greater Yellowstone Area. In response, the Forest Service limited numbers of domestic sheep on national forests and designated suitable pastures and travel routes. (Buechner 1960, Hawkes 1976, Smith 1982, Ryder and Lanka 1997, Smith 2002, Picton and Lonner 2008, Pioneer Society of Sweet Grass County 2008, Stryker 2009)

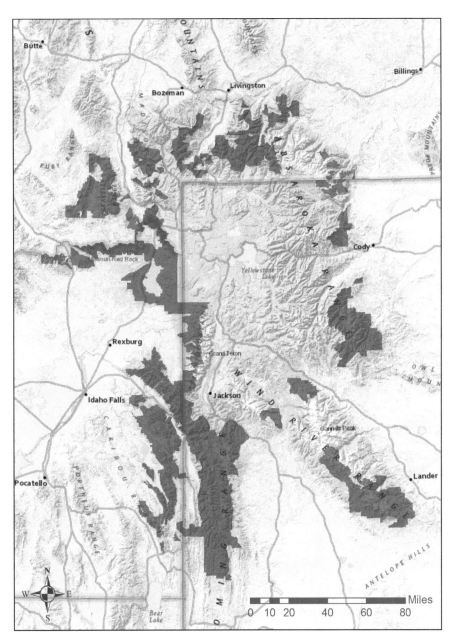

*Figure 2. Domestic sheep grazing allotments (bluish-gray shading) used at various times from the early 1900s to present on National Forest lands in the Greater Yellowstone Area. Map by Shannon Pils and Dan Tyers, U.S. Forest Service.*

Given this history, it is likely domestic sheep mixed with wild bighorn sheep on many of their seasonal ranges, as shown by documented cases of offspring from mating between wild bighorn and domestic sheep. While mixing, domestic sheep likely spread some diseases to bighorn sheep. As a result, most respiratory diseases in domestic sheep are present in bighorn sheep in the Greater Yellowstone Area. (Honess and Frost 1942, Edgar and Turnell 1979, Butler et al. 2017)

*It is likely all bighorn sheep herds in the Greater Yellowstone Area experienced commingling with domestic sheep during European settlement. As a result, some respiratory pathogens introduced at that time likely continue to circulate in certain bighorn sheep populations. Photo by Ed Arnett.*

## CONSERVATION EFFORTS

By the early 1900s, market hunting, habitat destruction, and diseases spread from livestock reduced numbers of bighorn sheep to the point where remaining populations were small and isolated. Efforts by conservation organizations and government agencies began to reverse this trend by limiting harvests and protecting habitat. Congress passed the Forest Reserve Act in 1891 and over the next 12 years Presidents Harrison, Cleveland, and Roosevelt designated more than 6.5 million acres (26,300 square kilometers) around Yellowstone National Park as public forests.

Congress established the National Forest Service in 1905 to manage these lands for multiple uses, including timber harvest and livestock grazing. Over time, the Forest Service refined their management focus to include public recreation and the conservation of wildlife and their habitats. (Buechner 1960, Hawkes 1976, USDA Forest Service 1978, Gill 2010, Wild Sheep Working Group 2015, Tyers et al. 2017)

In addition, sportsmen's groups encouraged proper hunting practices and urged legislatures to pass laws to limit harvests. Congress passed the Yellowstone National Park Protection Act in 1894 to ban hunting and the harassment of wildlife therein. The tourism industry began to grow, with railroads increasing visitation to about 335,000 people on western public lands by 1915, which increased support for the conservation of wildlife and their habitats. Moreover, conservation organizations and state wildlife agencies began to relocate bighorn sheep to areas where they no longer existed. (Rocky Mountain Elk Foundation and Conservation Visions 2006, Gill 2010, Tyers et al. 2017)

Congress passed the Wilderness Act in 1964 and the Endangered Species Act in 1973, which altered the grazing of federal lands in the Greater Yellowstone Area by domestic sheep. The listing of Yellowstone grizzly bears as a threatened species in 1975 mandated their protection and recovery. This action led to the removal of domestic sheep from many high-mountain pastures in the Greater Yellowstone Area to reduce the need to remove bears killing sheep. In addition, a collapsing wool market and difficulties in finding skilled herders discouraged livestock producers from continuing this industry. In 1978, most of the Absaroka and Beartooth ranges became designated wilderness managed by the Forest Service and domestic sheep grazing was no longer a high priority. By 1983, only three operators held permits to graze domestic sheep in these ranges. For contrast, the Forest Supervisor authorized the grazing of 110,000 sheep in the Absaroka National Forest during 1913. When the Forest Service later instituted a more formal grazing program, 25 to 30 permittees consistently brought 30,000 sheep into these mountains. The last year summer herders brought domestic sheep into that high country was in 2003. Through the collaborative efforts of a diverse group of stakeholders, there were no domestic sheep grazing on federal lands where native populations of bighorn sheep lived in Wyoming by 2017. (Hawkes 1976, USDA, Forest Service 1978, Drummond 1983)

From the 1920s to 1990, the states of Wyoming, Montana, and Idaho relocated almost 3,000 bighorn sheep within their borders, imported another 300 animals, and provided over 600 bighorn sheep for restoration efforts in other states. Throughout the western United States, there were almost 1,500 relocations involving 21,500 bighorn sheep. In response, bighorn sheep numbers increased. In addition, state agencies began relocating mountain goats to areas where they did not occur. During the 1940s and 1950s, biologists relocated mountain goats from western Montana into three mountain ranges north of Yellowstone National Park. They made seven releases of 65 mountain goats into the Beartooth Range during 1942 to 1953 and 4 releases of 57 mountain goats into the Madison Range during 1947 to 1959. They also made three releases of 23 mountain goats into the Absaroka Range during 1956 to 1958 (Figure 3; Honess and Frost 1942, Smith 1982, Lemke 2004, McWhirter 2004, Wild Sheep Working Group 2015).

There was a gradual increase in the numbers of mountain goats during the following decades, with descendants moving 30 to 53 miles (50 to 85 kilometers) from release sites to occupy all mountain ranges in the northern portion of the Greater Yellowstone Area. Biologists observed mountain goats in the Wyoming portion of the Beartooth Mountains during 1946 and counted about 100 mountain goats there during the 1970s. In addition, mountain goats moved into Yellowstone National Park through the Absaroka and Gallatin mountain ranges during the 1960s and were living and reproducing in the northeast and northwest portions of the park by the 1990s. Mountain goats continued to move southward through the Absaroka Range and biologists observed them in the Wind River area during the 1980s, which is about 80 miles (130 kilometers) from the release sites in Montana. (Laundré 1990, Varley 1996, Lemke 2004, McWhirter 2004, Flesch et al. 2016)

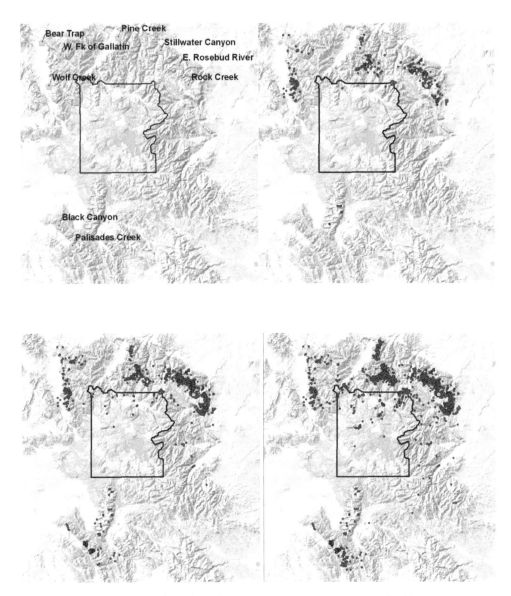

*Figure 3. Locations of the nine sites (green dots) where non-native mountain goats were introduced by state wildlife agencies into the Greater Yellowstone Area during the 1940s to the 1960s (top left panel) and their subsequent range expansion (red dots) through 1980 (top right), 1990 (bottom left), and 2000 (bottom right). Maps by Mike Sawaya, Montana State University.*

*Translocating mountain goats into the Greater Yellowstone Area required some resourceful thinking and unconventional techniques. Photo courtesy of Jim McLucas, Montana Fish, Wildlife and Parks.*

In 1969, biologists relocated five mountain goats from northern Idaho into the Palisades Creek area of the Snake River Range near the Idaho-Wyoming border. They observed mountain goats about 20 miles (32 kilometers) from the release site in the Snake River Canyon of Wyoming during 1975 and counted about 140 mountain goats in 1983. Biologists released seven mountain goats at Black Canyon in the Snake River Range during 1970-1971 but, apparently, these animals did not survive. During the 1980s, mountain goats thought to be descendants of the 1969 release moved 19 to 25 miles (30 to 40 kilometers) to the south and east in Wyoming. In 1986, there were about 230 mountain goats in this area. During the past 10 to 15 years, some mountain goats have moved northward into the Teton Range and Grand Teton National Park. (McWhirter 2004, Flesch et al. 2016)

## CURRENT STATUS

Today, there are about 50,000 Rocky Mountain bighorn sheep across western North America, which represents a 10-fold decrease from historic numbers, but an increase from the low of about 25,000 bighorn sheep in 1940. Factors slowing further recovery include widespread respiratory diseases that cause occasional die-offs, habitat loss, high predation in some areas, and disturbances from human recreational activities. There are about 5,600 to 5,900 bighorn sheep in the Greater Yellowstone Area, with about 4,000 animals in the Absaroka and Beartooth ranges of Wyoming along the eastern boundary of Yellowstone National Park. This population has relatively good reproduction and survival and few outbreaks of respiratory diseases. Only a small population of bighorn sheep remains in Grand Teton National Park. Similarly, most populations in Montana are isolated with less than 150 bighorn sheep. As a result, they may be susceptible to rapid decreases in numbers during disease outbreaks, severe weather events, or predation by cougars or golden eagles on lambs. (Buechner 1960, Toweill and Geist 1999, Festa-Bianchet et al. 2006, Hogg et al. 2006, Johnson et al. 2010, Butler et al. 2013, Flesch et al. 2016)

There are 1,600 to 2,300 mountain goats living in the Greater Yellowstone Area, with most being descendants of mountain goats released in Montana. Mountain goats have moved into, and numbers are increasing, in most areas occupied by bighorn sheep in the northern portion of the area, including in the Gallatin and Absaroka mountains (Figure 4). Numbers are lower in the Wyoming portion of the Snake River Range, but mountain goats have moved northward into the Teton Range and increased in numbers. Mountain goats have not yet moved into much of the southern portion of the Absaroka Range east of Yellowstone National Park in Wyoming, as well as the Gros Ventre and Wind River Ranges to the south. However, biologists expect them eventually to move into these areas. Thus, the numbers and distribution of mountain goats in the Greater Yellowstone Area likely will increase. (Flesch et al. 2016)

In recent decades, federal agencies have issued fewer grazing permits for domestic sheep in the Greater Yellowstone Area to lessen conflicts with grizzly bears and wolves and decrease the spread of diseases to bighorn sheep. Several groups, including the National Wildlife Federation, Sagebrush Fund, Conservation Fund, and Wild Sheep Foundation (and its' chapters in Wyoming, Montana, and Idaho) have paid ranchers to stop grazing on certain public lands. These agreements have removed livestock from almost 700,000 acres (283,280 hectares) in the Greater Yellowstone Area, thereby benefitting bighorn sheep and other wildlife, reducing conflicts, and providing other options to livestock producers. (Tyers et al. 2017, Wuerthner 2017, National Wildlife Federation 2018)

## CONCLUSIONS

Settlement and grazing by hundreds of thousands of domestic cattle and sheep brought the influence of many humans and livestock into the remote mountains of the Greater Yellowstone Area. These changes created an interesting chapter in the history of this region, but negatively affected native vegetation communities and

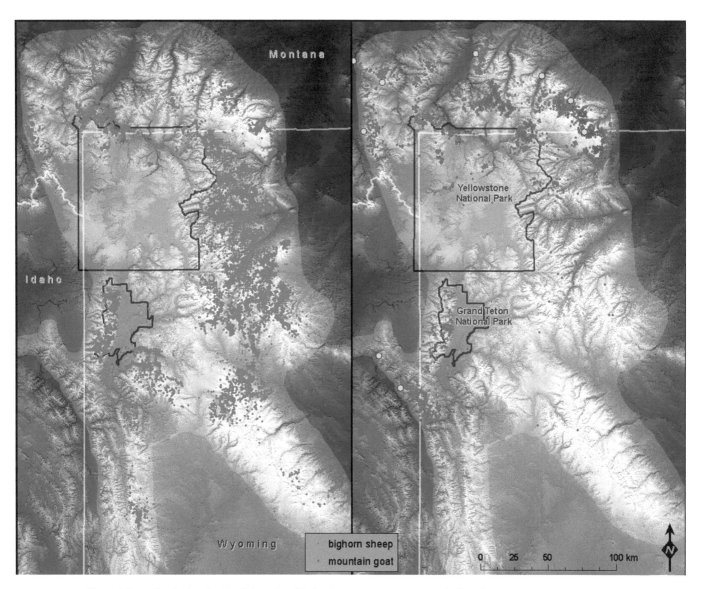

*Figure 4. Recent distribution of native bighorn sheep (blue) and non-native mountain goats (red) in the Greater Yellowstone Area based on more than 30,000 records collected by wildlife management agencies between 1937 and 2015 (from Flesch et al. 2016). Green dots depict mountain goat introduction sites. Maps by Jesse DeVoe.*

*A pair of mature bighorn rams. Photo by Shawn T. Stewart.*

wildlife such as bighorn sheep through habitat destruction, overgrazing, and disease transmission. Despite these lingering effects, the Greater Yellowstone Area still maintains one of the last remnants of wild America in the continuous United States. The rugged wilderness is relatively undisturbed compared to most other areas and protected from development.

Bighorn sheep and mountain goats have different histories in the Greater Yellowstone Area. Nearly a century of conservation efforts with bighorn sheep have had mixed results, with animals being numerous and broadly distributed in the eastern portion, less plentiful and more sparsely distributed in the northern and southern portions, and rare in the western portion. Numbers of bighorn sheep in or near Yellowstone National Park are still well below pre-settlement conditions based on written accounts from the 1800s. In contrast, the release of about 157 mountain goats in the area was quite successful, with animals expanding their distribution and numbers increasing to perhaps 2,000 over the past 50 years.

The expanding range of mountain goats in the Greater Yellowstone Area led to concerns about impacts to mountainous plants, competition for food with bighorn sheep, and the spread of diseases. Some biologists recommended removing mountain goats to keep them at low numbers and prevent further range expansion. However, many people like mountain goats and are skeptical they negatively affect native plants and wildlife. Thus, managers needed trustworthy information about competition, disease transmission, and resource use by mountain goats and bighorn sheep. (Schullery and Whittlesey 2001, Lemke 2004, National Park Service 2006, DeVoe 2015, Flesch et al. 2016, Whittlesey et al. 2018, Whittlesey and Bone 2020)

## HOW WE LEARN: USING HISTORIC WILDLIFE ACCOUNTS TO INFORM CONTEMPORARY MANAGEMENT

Describing historic wildlife communities is helpful for evaluating intervening changes and developing contemporary conservation objectives. The written record of conditions in the Greater Yellowstone Area prior to settlement by Euro-Americans consists mostly of accounts from colonists and travelers. Previous analyses of less than two dozen well-known accounts by scientists, advocates, and other commentators led to contradictory conclusions about the distribution of large mammals in the area. Some investigators maintained large mammals were absent or uncommon, while others concluded they were plentiful and widespread.

To resolve these contradictions, historians Lee Whittlesey and Paul Schullery compiled more than 800 accounts of wildlife in the area during 1796 to 1881 from books, government survey reports, guidebooks, journals, letters, maps, newspapers, photographs, and other periodical literature. A relational database was created in Microsoft Access® to summarize the information from each account and enable queries (see https://www.nps.gov/yell/learn/historyculture/upload/HistoricWildlife-ObservationsFlatFile.csv). Also, an ArcGIS® feature class was created to spatially locate each observation based on the precision of information provided by the observer.

These historical accounts indicated bears, bison, elk, wolves, and other large mammals were widespread in the Greater Yellowstone Area prior to Euro-American colonization and settlement (Figure 5). These casual observations could not be used to estimate population sizes, relative abundances, seasonal movements and migration routes, or periods of occupancy with certainty. However, the approach was useful for informing contemporary management issues regarding the seasonal distributions of large mammals and whether species such as mountain goats and wolves were present in the area. Similar efforts could clarify historic wildlife conditions elsewhere and provide reference information for modern conservation decisions (Whittlesey et al. 2018, Whittlesey and Bone 2020).

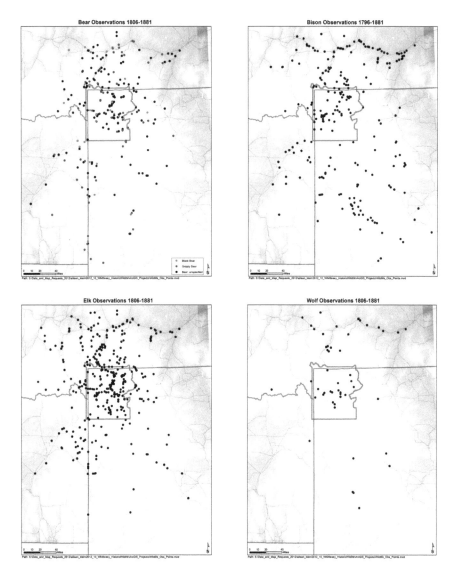

*Figure 5. Historical observations of bears, bison, elk, and wolves in the Greater Yellowstone Area during 1796-1881. The green outlines depict Yellowstone National Park, established in 1872, while the gray lines are the boundaries of Idaho, Montana, and Wyoming, established during 1889-1890. Maps by Allison Klein, National Park Service.*

*Adult male mountain goat, or billy, in its winter coat. Photo by Mark Gocke.*

# Chapter 3
# Seasonal Habitat Characteristics

*Blake Lowrey, Robert A. Garrott, Douglas E. McWhirter
and P. J. White*

## INTRODUCTION

Bighorn sheep and mountain goats occupy rugged, mountainous landscapes that add to their iconic character and inspire onlookers. They have behaviors and physical attributes suited for a life in steep terrain and are at ease crossing snow-covered slopes or standing atop a cliff precipice. They are also comfortable foraging, fighting for mates, or raising young in rugged, steep areas. However, bighorn sheep and mountain goats are not restricted to the mountains. Bighorn sheep also live in river canyons and on prairie breaks, while some mountain goats have expanded into canyon regions such as the Clark's Fork of the Yellowstone River in northwest Wyoming. Recent advances in global positioning system (GPS) technology and radio telemetry have enabled researchers to obtain a more detailed description of habitat use by animals in remote, rugged areas. This chapter provides a comprehensive characterization of the seasonal habitats used by bighorn sheep and mountain goats within the Greater Yellowstone Area.

## WHAT IS HABITAT?

The term habitat has a long and varied history with inconsistent usage. In this book, we define habitat as the collection of resources and conditions in an area that allow bighorn sheep and mountain goats to survive and reproduce. Habitat is more than a vegetation type, such as a prairie or forest, and includes components such as food, water, mineral licks, thermal cover, and shelter from predators or open areas where these mountain ungulates can detect predators. Just as a cougar needs an ample prey base to survive and reproduce, bighorn sheep and mountain goats need enough areas to evade predators where they can also find necessary food resources. Habitat use often varies between males and females due to their different physiological and biological needs as individuals try to acquire enough forage and other beneficial resources while minimizing the risk of predation or other threats. Habitat use also varies seasonally due to changes in environmental conditions and the availability and quality of resources. For example, a low-elevation meadow may provide habitat in winter with shelter from high-elevation snow and access to early emerging vegetation in spring. However, this same area may be inadequate in late summer when hot conditions dry out vegetation and cooler moister conditions at higher elevations result in greener vegetation. (Hall et al. 1997)

*Examples of high elevation (12,000 feet; Younts Peak at the headwaters of the Yellowstone River, left) and lower elevation (4,400 feet; Clarks Fork Canyon, right) habitats for bighorn sheep in the Greater Yellowstone Area. Photos by Doug McWhirter, Wyoming Game and Fish Department.*

Understanding the most important habitat attributes for mountain ungulates throughout the year is critical for their effective management and conservation. With this information, managers can maintain or enhance habitat through restoration projects to better support survival and reproduction. For example, where conifer encroachment is negatively affecting habitats for bighorn sheep, managers often use prescribed fires to increase visibility and improve habitat quality. Understanding habitat limitations also can help inform management actions. For example, managers have used water catchment systems and blocks of essential minerals to supplement and improve habitat conditions in some areas. Similarly, managers have increased harvests of predators to limit predation on sensitive bighorn sheep populations. While understanding wildlife-habitat relationships and conducting targeted restoration projects can be an effective management tool, managers cannot manipulate many important habitat attributes such as slope steepness, aspect, winter severity, or elevation. Nonetheless, knowledge of the relationship with these habitat components can help to identify areas for habitat manipulations and the restoration of populations. (Smith et al. 1999, Rominger et al. 2004, Longshore et al. 2009)

## CONDUCTING HABITAT RESEARCH

To understand how animals use habitats through the year, managers need to locate them frequently and characterize attributes such as topography, vegetation cover, and human alterations at each location. Historically, biologists obtained this information by driving and hiking to locate animals and describe habitat attributes, which limited study areas to places and seasons and time of day people could readily access. Recent advances in radio telemetry and remote sensing have improved the availability of data used to characterize wildlife habitat over broad, remote landscapes. Biologists can place global positioning system collars on captured animals and continually record locations at specified intervals for more than 5 years. In addition, data from satellites is now available to map habitat attributes across large regions. As a result, information on land cover type, percent canopy cover, elevation, slope steepness, moisture levels, vegetation greenness, roads, and other natural and human features are available across the globe.

Once managers have collected enough animal locations and associated habitat attributes, it is possible to characterize seasonal habitat preferences and develop models that predict habitat selection. These habitat models can inform management decisions in other populations or areas, such as whether to relocate animals into unoccupied areas to expand their distribution. Managers have used this practice to restore native bighorn sheep throughout the Greater Yellowstone Area and the western United States. (Brewer et al. 2014)

## Seasonal Habitat Associations

### Bighorn sheep

Except during the breeding period from mid-November to the end of January, bighorn sheep segregate on seasonal ranges with mature males aggregating in small groups and females, lambs, and young males occurring in larger social groups. Terrain features such as slope, ruggedness, and elevation are the most influential habitat attributes for bighorn sheep in both summer and winter. Bighorn sheep use a range of elevations from valley bottoms at 3,000 feet (900 meters) to high mountain peaks above 10,000 feet (3,000 meters). Generally, bighorn sheep summer ranges occur on relatively steep and rugged slopes at high elevations. In contrast, winter ranges are often within lower elevation valley bottoms with less snow accumulation. However, there is a wide range of variation in habitat preferences both within and among bighorn sheep populations within the Greater Yellowstone Area. For example, rather than migrate to lower elevations in winter, bighorn sheep in Grand Teton National Park and some animals throughout the Absaroka, Wind River, and Gros Ventre Mountains are high elevation residents and select for low angle windswept plateaus which remain relatively snow-free during the winter months. On average, bighorn sheep summer and winter ranges have slope angles of 40° and 35°, ranging between 12° to 40°. (Stewart 1975, Hurley 1985, Krausman and Bowyer 2003, Courtemanch et al. 2017, Lowrey et al. 2018b)

In the mountains, bighorn sheep graze on terraces, ledges, and grasslands where they can access ample forage, often within or adjacent to steep terrain. Bighorn sheep generally avoid areas with dense forests and are more strongly associated with open landscapes with herbaceous forage and few visibility obstructions. They mostly use cool, north-northwest aspects in summer, likely to help regulate body temperature and take advantage of greener vegetation later in the growing season when plants on hotter slopes begin to dry out. Conversely, in winter bighorn sheep select south-southwest aspects where there is less snow and easier access to forage. Seasonal ranges can overlap or be more than 30 miles (50 kilometers) apart depending on migratory tendencies (see chapter 4). (Stewart 1975, Krausman and Bowyer 2003, Courtemanch et al. 2017, Lowrey et al. 2018b)

*Examples of bighorn sheep summer (left) and winter (right) ranges in the Absaroka Range. Photos by Doug McWhirter, Wyoming Game and Fish Department.*

Biologists often use remote-sensing estimates of vegetation greenness, such as the normalized difference vegetation index (NDVI), to describe forage quality or quantity for ungulates. Somewhat counter to expectations, bighorn sheep often appear to select areas with lower vegetation greenness. While forage is obviously an important component of bighorn sheep habitat, their strong selection for steep and rugged slopes that are characteristically rocky and have relatively low greenness values likely conceals this relationship. Moreover, when selecting for forage resources bighorn sheep may be using forage patches such as ledges that are too small or intermittent to show up in remotely sensed satellite layers. (Pettorelli et al. 2011, Lowrey et al. 2017, 2018b)

Although most habitat-related research focuses on summer and winter as the seasonal periods, a few studies have characterized birthing and nursery sites. While this information is generally limited because of the difficulty in identifying such areas, understanding the habitat attributes associated with successful or unsuccessful birthing events is an important management objective. Bighorn sheep often use isolated, small ledges within steep terrain and with good visibility for birthing and nursery sites because of the vulnerability of lambs to predation. These areas can be nestled among vertical rocks walls with small terraces used for foraging in the weeks following birth. The use of such habitats offers the best predator avoidance strategy during the most vulnerable life stages. (Stewart 1975, Krausman and Bowyer 2003, Smith et al. 2015)

## MOUNTAIN GOATS

As relative newcomers within the Greater Yellowstone Area, and because they occur in low numbers within areas that are difficult to study, there has been little work describing mountain goat habitat. Most descriptions of mountain goat seasonal habitats have been within native ranges of British Columbia and southeast Alaska, often within coastal areas. Mountain goats display a wide range of individual responses to seasonal changes that can complicate the delineation of seasonal habitats for the entire population. Nonetheless, terrain variables strongly influence which areas mountain goats use within their varied seasonal ranges. (Poole and Heard 2003, Taylor and Brunt 2007, Rice 2008, Poole et al. 2009, White et al. 2012, DeVoe et al. 2015, Lowrey et al. 2017, 2018b)

A steep slope angle is the most influential habitat attribute in both seasons, with slopes on summer ranges averaging 37°. In winter, rather than selecting for an optimal slope angle, mountain goats seek out the steepest slopes, which in continental mountain ranges continually shed snow. This strategy reduces energy expenditure associated with movement and increases access to forge. During summer and winter, mountain goats use rugged areas with minimal canopy cover that are characteristic of the alpine environments where they reside. Like bighorn sheep, mountain goats show a seasonal response to aspect and select for cool, northeast aspects in summer and warm, southwest aspects in winter. The seasonal response is stronger for mountain goats than for bighorn sheep, and most pronounced in summer, likely a result of a reduced tolerance for hot summer temperatures. While bighorn sheep occur across a broad area from the deserts of northern Mexico to the Rocky Mountains of southern Canada, native ranges of mountain goats are limited to mountainous areas, predominantly in northwestern reaches of North America. Due to this closer association with colder climates, mountain goats may have a lower temperature threshold, which they maintain by selecting for cooler, northwest aspects during the warm summer months. Similar to bighorn sheep, mountain goats can have a negative relationship with various forage indices, although this is likely due to strong selection for rugged and rocky areas rather than a true avoidance of forage (Chadwick 2002, DeVoe et al. 2015, Lowrey et al. 2017, 2018b)

Beyond the general summer and winter seasonal periods, biologists know little about the specific habitat associations of mountain goat kidding or nursery areas in the Greater Yellowstone Area. Females seek out secluded areas for one to two

*Examples of mountain goat summer (above) and winter (below) habitats in the Absaroka Range, although animals often remain in these same areas year-round. Photos by Steve Ard, Tracker Aviation, Inc.*

weeks during the early spring to give birth. Such areas are often isolated ledges with enough early forage available on warm aspects within a broader rugged landscape. The seclusion not only helps to avoid predators, but the isolated ledges can help to contain young kids who are eager to explore the new surroundings. It also provides an important opportunity for nanny and kid to bond before rejoining the herd. Additionally, daily bed sites are an important seasonal habitat attribute for mountain goats. Bed sites are located on or near cliffs with a broad and clear view of the surroundings. Although males will bed by themselves or in small groups, bedding areas for females and kids need to accommodate larger groups. The most socially dominant individuals generally use preferred bedding sites. (Chadwick 2002, Côté and Festa-Bianchet 2003)

## Habitat Overlap

Although bighorn sheep and mountain goats have long occurred on overlapping native ranges within portions of western North America, mountain goats were historically absent or scarce in the Greater Yellowstone Area. The introduced and expanding mountain goat population has raised concerns that encroachment into areas occupied by native bighorn sheep may be detrimental to established populations. There is the potential for increased spatial overlap as mountain goats continue to expand, with the possibility of competition and the transfer of diseases detrimental to native bighorn sheep. (Adams et al. 1982, Gross 2001, Reed 2001, Lowrey et al. 2017)

An early conceptual model generalized across separated study areas suggested the extreme ends of most habitat attributes, such as terrain steepness, ruggedness, and snow cover, characterizes mountain goat habitat compared to bighorn sheep. We evaluated these predictions in the northeast portion of the Greater Yellowstone Area, which mountain goats have almost completely occupied for many decades and encompasses much of their overlapping range with bighorn sheep.

Although the summer habitat relationships were similar for both species, the winter habitat relationships indicated some evidence of separation. Bighorn sheep tended to use relatively low elevations compared to mountain goats and had a stronger avoidance of forests. In addition, mountain goat winter habitat had steeper slopes than bighorn sheep. Nonetheless, the observed differences for some habitat attributes did not result in substantial separation. Rather, the winter habitats of bighorn sheep and mountain goats broadly overlapped, especially on steep mid-elevation slopes. (Adams et al. 1982, Lowrey et al. 2018b)

Although habitats broadly overlap, it is still unclear if the close association between native bighorn sheep and introduced mountain goats can result in competition for resources. Because of the relatively low numbers of mountain ungulates in the region and the expansive mountain landscape, important habitat attributes may not be limited, which would lessen the chance for competition. This might be especially true on summer ranges. In addition, although bighorn sheep and mountain goats are often observed in the same area, more work is needed to describe the proximity and duration of comingling events and the potential for diseases to be transmitted between the two species. Nonetheless, there is evidence for such transmission in areas outside of the Greater Yellowstone Area. Although competition or disease transfer is possible in any season, the shared use of patchily distributed and oftentimes restricted winter ranges represents the most probable scenario of detrimental interactions between mountain goats and bighorn sheep. The increasing overlap between them is an urgent issue biologists are investigating in some locations throughout the region. Natural resource managers have initiated the removal of mountain goats from areas where native bighorn sheep are the management priority, such as in Grand Teton National Park, and managing for lower densities in others (see chapter 9). (Gross 2001, Lowrey et al. 2018b, Wolff et al. 2019)

## MINERAL LICKS

Mineral licks are important habitat features used by many ungulates to obtain minerals and nutrients that may be seasonally deficient in available forage. Licks generally occur as one of three types, dry-earth, wet muck, or rock-faces, and are often associated with small sites that promote mineral deposition such as benches, abrupt reductions in slope angle, and seeps or other areas of continual water deposition. Local differences in topography and mineral composition can result in different lick use patterns, with some licks used more often. In the field, biologists identify licks by numerous trails leading to depressions or excavations, often at the bases of trees that expose the root systems. Licks also occur in road cuts or other cliff areas. (Hebert and Cowan 1971, Poole et al. 2010)

Although licks may occur within individual seasonal home ranges, bighorn sheep and mountain goats make lengthy and direct movements to licks located outside of their seasonal ranges, often traveling from summer ranges back to lower-elevation winter ranges. For example, mountain goats in the Snake River Range make repeat visits during the spring and early summer to a lick roughly 3 miles (5 kilometers) beyond their traditional seasonal ranges. Additionally, mountain goats in this population are often seen licking salt from Highway 89 through the Snake River Canyon east of Alpine, Wyoming in winter. Bighorn sheep in the Gros Ventre Mountains northeast of Jackson, Wyoming repeat their roughly 7-mile (11-kilometer) spring migration route multiple times throughout the spring and summer months for brief visits to their winter ranges, likely to access licks associated with road cuts along the Gros Ventre River.

The timing and duration of lick use varies within and among bighorn sheep and mountain goat populations. In general, the use of licks peaks in the spring and early summer due to a combination of depleted essential nutrients after poorer winter diets and the accessibility of licks, which are often buried under deep snow in winter.

*Bighorn sheep ram at a mineral lick, illustrating the attractiveness of such sites to mountain ungulates. Photo by Mark Gocke.*

Outside of the Greater Yellowstone Area, studies indicate males are often the first to access licks and female use coincides with birth and lactation. (Hebert and Cowan 1971, Poole et al. 2010)

Traveling to licks outside seasonal home ranges poses increased risk as the routes often cut through forested landscapes where vision is limited and there are relatively few terrain features for escape from predators. Nonetheless, the routine use of licks by mountain ungulates highlights their importance in maintaining sodium (salt) balance to aid electrolyte retention and support lactation in females. In addition, magnesium from licks can offset high levels of potassium and the associated reduction in absorption and retention of other elements. Furthermore, carbohydrates from licks can help stabilize rumen pH. (Ayotte et al. 2006 and references therein, Poole et al. 2010)

The limited and point source nature of licks may represent the most likely situation in which bighorn sheep and mountain goats come into direct contact. While mountain goats appear to be socially dominant, it is unclear how often direct encounters occur or the nature of such meetings. Nonetheless, licks may provide an increased opportunity for disease transfer between mountain ungulates or direct competition for a limited resource. The use of cameras placed at mineral licks may further our understanding of the behavioral interactions between bighorn sheep and mountain goats when seeking a shared, but limited, resource. To this end, biologists in Grand Teton National Park are placing cameras at many of the more than 15 known licks within the park. At present, bighorn sheep predominantly use the licks, although use by mountain goats may increase as the new arrivals have time to locate and exploit licks on the landscape. (Hebert and Cowan 1971, Poole et al. 2010, Lowrey et al. 2018b)

## HUMAN DISTURBANCE AND HABITAT CONCERNS

Although largely associated with mountain environments in wilderness areas with relatively little human disturbance, mountain ungulate habitat degradation or loss resulting from both direct and indirect human activities is an important concern throughout the Greater Yellowstone Area. Disturbances on winter ranges are particularly important because of their limited distribution and increased sensitivity to additional stresses during the harsh winter months. The inner-mountain west, particularly the Greater Yellowstone Area, is rapidly changing and experiencing some of the highest human population growth in the western United States. The associated development is predominately within valley bottoms and can have a direct impact on wild animals. (Baron 2002)

One unanticipated impact of the increase in people is the deposition and concentration of human urine in areas with high recreation activity. In addition to naturally occurring licks, mountain goats will seek out human urine to satisfy their craving for salt and other minerals. In areas like Glacier and Olympic national parks, habituated mountain goats aggressively approach people in search of urine and a hiker in Olympic National Park was fatally injured. As a result, managers in Olympic National Park began a massive translocation effort in August of 2019 to remove over 300 goats, sighting their non-native status and aggressive behavior towards tourists. While mountain goat habituation is currently not a major concern in Yellowstone National Park, increases in visitation could bring additional challenges in the future. Moreover, the issue of habituation may become problematic in Grand Teton National Park due to the heavy backcountry use by visitors climbing many of the park's granite peaks.

Human development associated with continued growth in the Greater Yellowstone Area can also have direct impacts on mountain ungulate habitat. Historically, the population of bighorn sheep in Grand Teton National Park was partially migratory, with both high-elevation residents and individuals that seasonally migrated between high-elevation summer ranges and low-elevation winter ranges. Because of the cumulative effects of human development, such as roads, fences, housing, and domestic livestock grazing on low-elevation winter habitat, the migrant component no longer persists. Today, bighorn sheep in Grand Teton National Park are resident at high elevations year-round and forgo a seasonal migration to historic low-elevation winter ranges. In other areas with less direct habitat loss, winter activities such as backcountry skiing and snowmobiling, ice climbing, or antler hunting may negatively impact habitat and result in short- or long-term range abandonment. Mountain goats, because they tend to remain on steep mid-elevation slopes during winter, may be less susceptible to human development and other activities. However, roads and other disturbances can negatively affect them in proximity to human development. In addition, the proximity to domestic livestock is an important consideration for mountain ungulates. Overgrazing by livestock could have negative impacts on plant communities, and provide a source of competition when ranges overlap (see chapters 2 and 9). (Whitfield 1983, White et al. 2012, Courtemanch et al. 2017, White and Gregovich 2017)

Exotic weeds and conifer encroachment are two additional factors that can reduce habitat quality, often on low-elevation winter ranges. The spread of non-native invasive plants can reduce forage quality and the persistence of green forage on the landscape. Moreover, conifer encroachment has reduced habitat quality in many areas, prompting the use of prescribed fire to restore habitat.

Negative impacts are not specific to low-elevation ranges. For example, bighorn sheep wintering at high elevations in Grand Teton National Park avoid disturbances associated with winter recreation such as backcountry skiing and snowboarding, resulting in a 30% reduction in available high-quality habitat for some individuals. Additionally, helicopter noise associated with heli-skiing can negatively affect mountain goats and result in increased movement rates and associated energy expenditure for up to two days after a fly over. Heli-skiing operations also increase the number of recreationists in mountain areas, potentially resulting in range reductions in areas with continued disturbance. (Cadsand 2012, Côté et al. 2013, Courtemanch 2014)

*Examples of potential disturbances to mountain ungulates and their habitat, including backcountry skiing, roads, human developments, and motorized recreation. Animals can habituate to very predictable disturbances but have been shown to avoid high quality habitats if disturbance is unpredictable and too frequent. Photos by Mark Gocke.*

Mountain ungulates are susceptible to habitat changes associated with climate change because they are mountain specialists. The high-mountain environments on which mountain ungulates depend will likely see notable changes in average annual temperatures, which have already increased 1.3°C from 1900 to 2000. Future projections indicate the increases in temperature will be greater for winter than for summer. The associated changes to mountain systems will likely have dynamic and opposing impacts on the habitat attributes of bighorn sheep and mountain goats. For example, an increase in winter temperatures may reduce snow accumulation and increase access to forage. However, warmer temperatures increase the frequency of hardened snow events that can reduce access to forage through producing impenetrable ice layers over broad geographic areas. Understanding climate-driven impacts to mountain ungulate habitat is an important research and management priority considering future climate projections within their sensitive mountain environment. (Hansen et al. 2006, Pederson et al. 2010, White et al. 2017)

## Conclusions

Bighorn sheep and mountain goats have evolved to occupy steep and rugged habitats for all aspects of their natural history. More than any other North American mammal, these animals exemplify an iconic existence in rugged landscapes. Such areas provide a reduced threat from predation in combination with ample forage resources, enabling bighorn sheep and mountain goats to persist in areas that other large mammals only seasonally occupy. Terrain features largely define seasonal habitats. While these mountain ungulates show differences in preference for some habitat attributes, their habitat largely overlaps seasonally. Thus, the introduced and expanding nature of mountain goats within this region is an important management issue (see chapters 8 and 9). Balancing different management objectives across the many jurisdictions in the Greater Yellowstone Area, while simultaneously incorporating diverse public opinions, is an urgent challenge within the region.

## HOW WE LEARN: TECHNOLOGY FOR TRACKING ANIMALS TO UNDERSTAND HOW THEY USE HABITATS

Although the idea of instrumenting animals with tracking devices is not new, there have been tremendous advances in Global Positioning System (GPS) technology in a relatively short period. Historically, researchers would place colored neck bands on individuals that were of research interest. While the simple bands did not actively track animal movements, the unique colors and patterns could help to identify animals when spotted later. Simple color bands were then replaced by Very High Frequency (VHF) collars which emit a consistent beep that is audible when tuned into a specific frequency using a receiver. Like with the colored neck bands, VHF transmitters do not actively record animal locations, yet were an important advancement in enabling researchers to relocate collared individuals. Very high frequency transmitters are still widely used in animal tracking but are often paired with a GPS device that actively records animal locations at pre-programmed intervals. There are numerous variations of GPS collars, for example some record locations and store the information on the unit, which then releases from the animal at a predetermined date and needs to be recovered from the field. Other GPS collars can communicate with researcher's computers via satellite and provide locations in nearly real-time.

Global positioning collars have helped to provide the continuous monitoring over multiple years that has advanced our understanding of animal habitat. The sample of GPS locations can be imported into a Geographic Information System (GIS) and intersected with various remote sensing layers to describe the environmental conditions of the areas used by collared animals (Figure 1). In addition, GPS locations can be separated into various groupings such as seasons or sexes to create different habitat models to meet multiple research objectives.

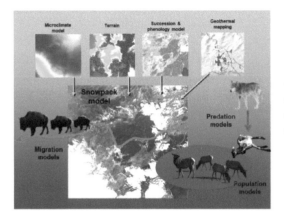

Figure 1. Animal locations from Global Positioning System (GPS) telemetry collars can be intersected with remote sensing layers from a Geographic Information System (GIS) to improve our understanding of the ecosystem and predict future dynamics and trends. Figure by Bob Garrott, Montana State University.

Fitting bighorn sheep and mountain goats with Global Positioning System (GPS) radio-collars to allow detailed monitoring of movements. Photos by Mark Gocke, Wyoming Game and Fish Department.

*A trio of bighorn sheep rams in winter. Photo by Kenneth R. Whitten.*

# Chapter 4
# Mountain Ungulate Migration

*Blake Lowrey, Douglas E. McWhirter,*
*Robert A. Garrott, and P. J. White*

## INTRODUCTION

Migration is widespread across many different types of animals. From insects and fish to birds and whales, the migratory movement of animals is an awe-inspiring behavior that evokes curiosity. Why would millions of birds travel thousands of miles between sub-Saharan Africa and Europe to breed? How did such a migration start? How do animals find the same breeding ground year after year? What cues determine migration timing? The questions are endless and the answers, when known, often vary according to the type of animal.

People in different fields use the word migration with varying definitions. In wildlife, migration refers to an animal behavior involving repeated seasonal movements of individuals between distinct seasonal ranges. Migration requires a round-trip movement, usually leaving a winter range in spring, traveling to a summer range, and returning to winter range in the fall. In most mammals, a single individual completes multiple migrations over the course of their lifetime. (Dingle and Drake 2007)

For migration to persist there needs to be some benefit to migratory individuals. For most animals, migrations are associated with gaining access to favorable resources or conditions. For example, while mountain environments can provide access to forage during the summer months, winter conditions can be inhospitable for most animals due to the cold temperatures and snow accumulation. Similarly, while low-elevation areas can provide a relatively mild winter climate and access to forage during the winter months, these areas can be inhospitable during summer when increased temperatures dry out forage. Rather than stay resident in any one area, migration and the movement between seasonally productive areas has evolved as a behavior that can increase individual survival and reproduction. Although distances between seasonal ranges can be substantial, the costs of migrating can be offset by the benefits of inhabiting seasonally productive ranges and result in increased survival or reproduction, thus allowing migration to persist over time. (Fryxell and Sinclair 1988, Fryxell et al. 1988, Dingle and Drake 2007)

Recent work on migratory ungulates in the western United States and the Greater Yellowstone Area has highlighted the importance of learning, memory, and social communication as the primary mechanisms influencing the development of migratory behavior. A newborn fawn, for example, will follow its mother on its first fall and spring migrations and remember the routes, which are then passed on through mother-daughter associations as well as social learning of migratory routes by following the herd. These insights, in large part, result from advances in Global Positioning System (GPS) devices, which allow researchers to track and map animal movements, and in some instances, follow animals in real-time. While researchers do not know what cues ungulates use in navigation, GPS collars have detailed their extraordinary ability to follow migratory routes, even if the route has only been traveled a single time previously. (Jesmer et al. 2018, Jakopak et al. 2019, Lowrey et al. 2019, Merkle et al. 2019)

Bighorn sheep and mountain goats are considered migratory, although both species have different migratory behaviors with varying reliance on migration annually. Moreover, both species show a large degree of variation in migratory behaviors among populations as well as locally among individuals within a population. In this chapter, we use data from our long-term study on mountain ungulates in the Greater

*Bighorn sheep ewe with lamb. Ungulate seasonal movements must be learned, and are passed down from mothers to their young. Photo by Mark Gocke, Wyoming Game and Fish Department.*

Yellowstone Area to broadly describe bighorn sheep and mountain goat migratory behaviors and their diversity. Additionally, we discuss threats to migration across the region and implications for restoring migration in areas where it has been lost or greatly reduced.

## BIGHORN SHEEP MIGRATIONS

Bighorn sheep in the Greater Yellowstone Area exhibit a variety of seasonal movement behaviors, from traveling through multiple drainages over distances exceeding 30 miles (50 kilometers) to traveling relatively short distances up and down a mountain to occupy different elevations seasonally (Figure 1). In addition, on both high and low elevations there can be segments of the population that do not migrate, but instead stay resident on single year-round range. Biologists refer to populations in which some individuals migrate between seasonal ranges and others remain resident on a single year-round range as partially migratory. This behavior is common in migratory species. Perhaps the most common bighorn sheep migration involves movements from low-elevation winter ranges that experience less snow and offer more foraging opportunities during the harsh winter months to high-elevation, alpine summer ranges. Within this general strategy, however, there are numerous variations. Some animals make extensive movements between summer and winter ranges. In addition, there are a few examples in the Greater Yellowstone Area of non-migratory bighorn sheep that reside year-round on low-elevation ranges. However, it is more common for residents to remain at high-elevations year-round. (Chapman et al. 2011)

One of the longest known bighorn sheep migrations in the Greater Yellowstone Area begins on winter range near the mouth of the Clarks Fork Canyon in Wyoming. From here animals travel northward across the Beartooth Plateau into Montana, crossing Rock Creek and into the East Rosebud drainage before crossing the upper reaches of the Clarks Fork of the Yellowstone River and ascending the slopes of Pilot and

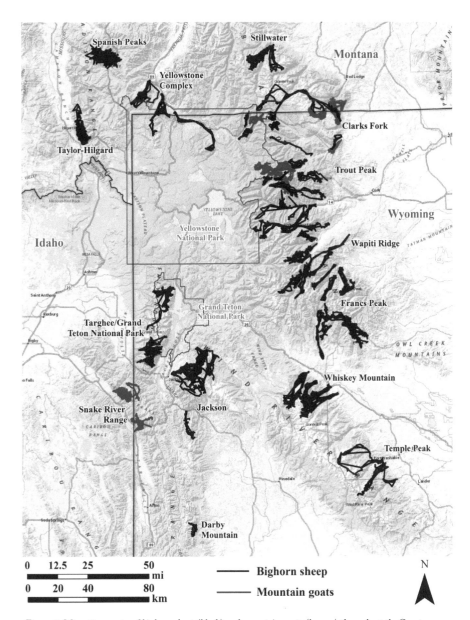

*Figure 1. Migration routes of bighorn sheep (black) and mountain goats (brown) throughout the Greater Yellowstone Area. Summer and winter ranges for migrant populations are not shown, but generally surround the starting and ending points of each migratory route. Migration routes represent known movements from GPS-collared individuals. There are likely other routes that were not documented from the sample of collared animals, especially for mountain goats which were only collared in a few populations. Figure by Blake Lowrey, Montana State University.*

Index peaks to summer along the eastern boundary of Yellowstone National Park. This long-distance migration "connects" non-migratory animals that reside year-round on the south facing slopes near the mouth of the Clarks Fork Canyon with other non-migratory animals that reside year-round on ranges surrounding Pilot Peak. The migration is over 30 miles (50 kilometers) long and bighorn sheep complete it in 7 to 14 days. What causes individuals that share summer ranges or winter ranges to migrate or not raises interesting questions, but likely relates to behaviors they learned from their mothers or others within their social group. (Jesmer at al. 2018, Lowrey et al. 2019)

An important behavioral strategy of many bighorn sheep in the Greater Yellowstone Area is spending winter at high elevations, oftentimes at elevations up to 12,000 feet (3,600 meters). These animals rely on extreme winds that blow the dry snow and expose forage on ridgetops and the edges of plateaus through mid to late winter. As wetter, heavier, spring snows accumulate, these sheep move downward to feed in areas of greening vegetation below the snowline at lower elevations. Sometimes called a "reverse migration," this situation is dependent upon a delicate interplay of factors that could be disrupted by changing temperatures and foraging conditions at either high or low elevations. (Courtemanch et al. 2017)

Although rams, ewes, and lambs often use the same migration corridors, rams will sometimes depart and travel to other areas during the November breeding season. This serves to increase genetic interchange among different population segments of bighorn sheep. This is illustrated by a collared ram that left ewe-lamb groups near the Washakie Needles and Wind River Reservation areas of the Owl Creek Mountains in mid-November and made a circuitous 30 mile (50 kilometer) semi-circle movement to breed ewes just north of Dubois, Wyoming in the Wiggins Fork drainage. By early December, the ram had traveled back to the Owl Creek Mountains to rejoin the same group he had departed from nearly a month earlier.

Seasonal movements of bighorn sheep include following the receding snowline in the spring, which allows for access to green and growing forage as they travel (usually upward in elevation) toward their alpine summer ranges. For bighorn sheep that spend winter at high elevations, however, springtime means dropping out of the deepening snow and accessing the green and growing forage below the snowline. Although quite variable from location-to-location and year-to-year, departure from low-elevation winter ranges usually occurs in May, with lambing occurring in late May and early June. Lambs are quick to gain their footing and stamina, and follow their mothers to summer ranges, which are sometimes quite distant. Bighorn sheep remain on their summer ranges until accumulating snow and deteriorating foraging conditions require them to move, which usually occurs in late October and into November. Most animals will arrive on low-elevation winter ranges for the mid-November breeding season, although some remain on high-elevation ranges for the rut and may even move up in elevation to wind-swept plateaus and ridges for the winter.

## Mountain Goat Migrations

Although mountain goats are considered migratory, their seasonal migrations are less defined and often occur over shorter distances than the migrations of bighorn sheep or other ungulates. Mountain goats generally do not undertake long-distance seasonal migrations between discrete or well-defined seasonal ranges. More often, mountain goat migrations are characterized by elevational movements between mid-elevation winter ranges that occur in pockets of steep terrain that continually shed snow over the winter months and summer ranges that are broadly distributed in high mountain environments. Unlike the large grouped migrations observed in other ungulates occupying African savannahs, the central Asian plateau, and Arctic tundra and boreal regions, in which many thousands of individuals travel *en masse* over broad landscapes, mountain goat migrations are characterized by solitary movements, especially for adult males, or small family and social groups migrating together.

*Mountain goat nanny with kid. Seasonal movements of mountain goats (if they occur at all) are characterized by solitary movements of individuals, or small family or social groups, and tend to be much more abbreviated than that of bighorn sheep. Photo by Mark Gocke, Wyoming Game and Fish Department.*

Within the Snake River Range, in the southwest portion of the Greater Yellowstone Area, mountain goat winter and summer ranges are at 6,500 feet (2,000 meters) and 9,000 feet (2,750 meters), respectively. The migrations between the separate seasonal ranges are relatively short and characterized by an average distance of 3 miles (5 kilometers; Figure 1). Although the migratory paths and seasonal ranges may vary from year-to-year, nearly all individuals migrate in this area. The migratory paths are steep, and most mountain goats traverse the elevational gradient in a few days. In addition, mountain goats in the Snake River Range are known to seek out salt and other minerals along U.S. Highway 26 in the Snake River Canyon east of Alpine, Wyoming. While these mineral resources are most commonly accessed during the winter and spring months, it is not uncommon for individuals to make short-term trips from summer ranges back to mid- or low-elevation ranges.

Migrations in the Teton, northern Absaroka, and Beartooth mountains are more variable. On average, seasonal ranges in these areas are higher than in the Snake River Range. Migrant individuals move between winter ranges around 8,000 feet (2,500 meters) and summer ranges close to 10,000 feet (3,000 meters) and span a range of distances from only a few miles to over 15 miles (24 kilometers). These distances can be covered in a few days to a few weeks. In addition to migrants, other individuals stay resident at high elevations year-round. Rather than migrate between discrete ranges in response to seasonal weather patterns, resident individuals have shorter but more frequent movements, likely reflecting individual responses to more variable daily or weekly weather events.

## MIGRATORY DIVERSITY

Migratory diversity refers to the proportion of individual migratory behaviors within a population. Populations with high migratory diversity contain different individuals that perform different types of migratory behaviors that result in varying movement and distribution patterns across the landscape. For example, there can be short- and long-distance migrants, as well as year-round residents which can occur at high and low elevations. In contrast, populations with limited migratory diversity contain individuals with only a single or relatively few migratory behaviors. For many different types of migratory animals, the varied spatial patterns associated with multiple migratory behaviors in a population can result in a broad and diffuse distribution across seasonal ranges. For example, rather than all individuals having the same migration between the same seasonal ranges as in populations with low migratory diversity, the varied migratory behaviors associated with high migratory diversity can increase the number of seasonal ranges for a population as well as their separation. The broad and diffuse distribution on the landscape can provide a buffer from human disturbances as well as increase genetic diversity and population stability. In contrast, when all or most individuals have the same migratory movements, individuals are subject to the same conditions and can be more susceptible to local conditions or disturbances. In years when environmental conditions are poor, the entire population may be negatively impacted. (Schindler et al. 2015b, Finch et al. 2016, Gilroy et al. 2016)

In bighorn sheep, a population's management history strongly influences the amount of time animals have had to learn landscape patterns and migratory routes. Native populations that have never been extirpated from the landscape have retained the historic herd 'knowledge' of migratory behaviors which developed over thousands of years. In contrast, knowledge of historic migratory behaviors has been lost in restored populations which were extirpated from the landscape and then repopulated by moving animals from different areas. Moving animals from other areas is a practice that has been foundational to bighorn sheep restoration and has resulted in increases in abundance and distribution regionally. However, this practice has not successfully recreated migratory patterns in restored or augmented populations. As a result, most native populations contain complex and dynamic seasonal movement patterns in which a single population is characterized by many different groups of animals,

*Bighorn sheep migrating to winter range in the Absaroka Mountains. Native populations that have never been extirpated exhibit more diverse movement patterns compared to restored populations, which tend to exhibit the same short-distance migrations or exhibit no migratory behavior at all. Photo by Travis Zaffarano, University of Wyoming.*

called subpopulations, often with multiple migratory behaviors that are broadly distributed over the population's range. In contrast, restored populations are often characterized by a single seasonal range with most animals being resident or exhibiting the same migratory behavior. (Jesmer et al. 2018, Lowrey et al. 2019)

## SUMMER MIGRATIONS

Migration is most often thought of as a movement between seasonal ranges (from winter range to summer range and returning to winter range over the course of year), but there are other round-trip movements that occur within the summer season. For example, Whiskey Mountain bighorn sheep routinely leave their alpine summer

*Images taken from remote-triggered cameras at known mineral lick sites. Upper left shows a nannie mountain goat digging at the lick site with kid nearby. This lick was frequented by mountain lions (lower left). Image on the right shows a ewe bighorn sheep standing to reach a known lick in Grand Teton National Park. Photos by Carson Butler, National Park Service.*

ranges and return to mineral deposits on their low-elevation winter ranges 10 miles (16 kilometers) away. Similarly, mountain goats in the Snake River Range routinely travel 5 miles (8 kilometers) to visit a specific mineral lick located well outside their summer range. In addition to the documented movements to known mineral licks, movement data collected from GPS-collared bighorn sheep and mountain goats throughout the Greater Yellowstone Area have documented a similar pattern. For many populations of animals spending summer on high-elevation ranges there are often relatively rapid and directed trips to low-elevation sites on their winter ranges that last for only a few days before quickly returning to summer range. When visiting lick sites animals consume soil or soft rock, a behavior called geophagia. Chemical analyses of some of these lick sites indicate the consumed materials have high concentrations of sodium, calcium, phosphorous, magnesium, and other elements which are trace minerals essential for supporting important physiological processes. (Mincher et al. 2008, Slabach et al. 2015)

All animals have specific requirements for trace minerals which are usually obtained from their diets. However, plants consumed by bighorn sheep and mountain goats do not always satisfy their needs for all trace minerals, which can have negative impacts on an animal's health. Trace mineral deficiencies in wild ungulates are believed to be most acute during the spring and summer months when animals transition from low quality, dormant winter forage to highly nutritious growing plants in spring and early summer. Green plants in early spring have high concentrations of potassium which can force animals to shed other nutrients and result in deficiencies in several trace minerals. In addition, females that give birth to lambs and kids in spring have additional requirements for trace minerals to support the production of milk to nurse their young. (Ayotte et al. 2006, Mincher et al. 2008)

While traveling to lick sites to satisfy trace mineral deficiencies provides important health benefits, there are also some potential negative consequences. The short-duration summer migrations commonly performed by mountain ungulates throughout the Greater Yellowstone Area present significant energy expenditures and place the animals at heightened risk of predation as the paths traveled typically include movements through forested habitat distant from the open, rugged landscapes that help their ability to detect predators and avoid attacks. Lambs and kids following their mothers are probably the most vulnerable.

Like seasonal migrations between summer and winter ranges, young animals probably learn the location of mineral licks by following their mothers or social groups. This suggests that when managers attempt to reintroduce animals into landscapes where they have been extirpated, a common practice for bighorn sheep restoration, the animals may lack knowledge of the locations of the small features on the landscape that represent sources of the trace minerals essential for physiological health.

## THREATS TO MIGRATION

Conserving animal migration has been noted as one of the most difficult conservation challenges of the 21st century. Globally, habitat loss, barriers along migratory routes, overexploitation, and climate change have resulted in steep declines of migratory behavior, and for many species, subsequent population declines. The loss of migration has important implications not only for wildlife ecology and management, but for humans. For example, pollination of many of the nation's crops are reliant on migratory insects, many of which are in decline. Once lost, restoring migrations has been met with limited success, as the cause of the initial extirpation, such as habitat loss or fragmentation, can persist on the landscape. Although a few hopeful examples have demonstrated some capacity to restore migrations after removing landscape barriers to animal movement, the gains generally come at high economic costs and represent a diminished resemblance of historic migratory patterns. (Ellis et al. 2003, Wilcove and Wikelski 2008, Bartlam-Brooks et al. 2011)

Landscape development is the biggest factor contributing to migration loss in the Greater Yellowstone Area. The inter-mountain west is one of the fastest growing regions in the western United States. As urban areas continue to expand and become denser, they are less permeable to wildlife. Landscape features such as roads, housing development, natural resource extraction facilities and infrastructure, and fences all negatively impact migration regionally. Although many mountain ungulates spend summer in high mountain environments, they generally spend winter at lower elevations that are more susceptible to human development. Moreover, as urban areas continue to expand into the urban-wildland interface, movements between seasonal ranges are increasingly difficult. For example, development surrounding the Teton Range has negatively impacted low-elevation bighorn sheep winter ranges and cut off historic migration routes from low-elevation winter ranges to high-elevation summer ranges. As a result, today only a high-elevation resident population persists in the Teton Range. In addition, expanding human habitation of winter range

*Loss of migration to lower elevation habitats has left sheep in the Tetons to reside on high-elevation habitats year-round. Photo by Mark Gocke, Wyoming Game and Fish Department.*

habitats can increase risk of contracting new pathogens (disease-causing agents) from domestic livestock, which can result in disease outbreaks, population declines, and loss of migratory diversity. (Whitfield 1983, Courtemanch et al. 2017)

The benefits of migration depend on a delicate balance between changing temperatures and foraging conditions at either high or low elevations. As climate change continues to alter these patterns, especially in mountain environments, migration timing and the associated benefits may change under future climate conditions. Shorter growing seasons, faster green-up periods, or more severe weather events can all negatively impact wildlife, but migrants, because of their unique dependence on landscape patterns and timing, are more susceptible to climatic changes.

## Conserving Migration

Interest in migration has seen a steady increase since the broad use of GPS and geolocation technology in animal research. These relatively new technologies allow researchers to passively track animals and map their locations frequently and accurately. Knowing where animals migrate and what routes are used is a critical step in conserving migration. As tracking devices continue to get smaller with prolonged battery life, researchers can track many different types of animals for longer periods. This information is critical for both conservation and research. The simple act of making maps of animal migration not only helps managers document migration routes but maps also help to garner public interest in migration, as well as develop options for their conservation. Conserving migration corridors was recently formalized as an important management priority for state and federal agencies across the western United States. (Wyoming Game and Fish Department 2016, U.S. Department of the Interior 2018)

Using tracking technologies to determine and map migration can help target specific areas for conservation projects such as fence removal, conservation easements, or policy changes to guide impacts of human disturbances. As larger datasets become available, finding similarities across species can further identify important areas and direct conservation efforts. Additionally, managers can use larger datasets to better understand migratory behavior and anticipate and mediate the effects of climate change or other threats to migration. (Fryxell and Sinclair 1988, Helfield and Naiman 2001, Dingle and Drake 2007)

## Conclusions

Bighorn sheep and mountain goats are both considered migratory ungulates. Bighorn sheep have more pronounced migrations between discrete seasonal ranges that can be simple elevational movements over relatively short distances to long migrations over 30 miles (50 kilometers) that traverse complex landscapes and multiple drainages. Mountain goat migrations are generally shorter and characterized by elevational movements but can also be upwards of 15 miles (24 kilometers) in length. Both species have partially migratory populations in which some individuals remain resident on a single range while others migrate seasonally. Habitat loss and alteration, barriers along migratory routes, and climate change pose the biggest threats to migration regionally. As GPS technology continues to advance, managers can use larger datasets to better understand migratory behavior and anticipate and mediate the effects of climate change and other threats toward migration. Maps of animal migration will help document migratory routes and inform targeted conservation efforts.

## How We Learn: Using GPS Technology to Understand Animal Migration

Global positioning system (GPS) collars have revolutionized many aspects of wildlife research and can allow nearly continuous monitoring of animals in real-time. Prior to GPS tracking devices, obtaining a location from an animal collared with a very high frequency (VHF) transmitter would entail a broad survey from the ground or a fixed-wing aircraft. Such surveys were time consuming or expensive and often conducted only once a month or, if lucky, once a week. The course survey intervals could help to determine if a collared individual migrated if they were relocated in a different seasonal range but provided little other information. For example, the dates when an animal departed one seasonal range and arrived at another, the distances traveled, or the migratory routes were not accurately captured with monthly or even weekly aerial surveys. The development of GPS collars helped to fill a large information gap with respect to animal migration. For the first time, biologists could see clear migratory routes by connecting the GPS locations collected with shorter time intervals, on the order of daily or hourly locations, and identify migration timing, duration, and distance.

The bighorn sheep migration from winter ranges along the Beartooth Plateau to the areas surrounding Pilot Peak is one of the longest documented bighorn sheep migrations (Figure 2). Early work with VHF collars documented migrations between these two areas, but not until the deployment of GPS collars did biologists get the full picture. Figure 2 shows the GPS locations (collated every 5 hours and connected by lines) of a single female bighorn sheep collared as part of our research efforts in the Greater Yellowstone Area. The individual left her winter range on June 8th and migrated over 30 miles (50 kilometers), arriving at the summer range on June 15th, after an 8-day spring migration. She stayed on summer range until beginning her fall migration on October 10th and nearly

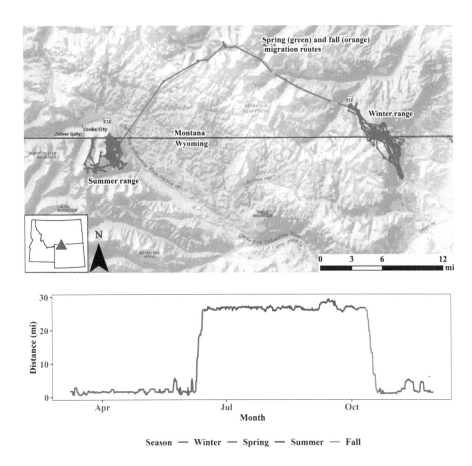

*Figure 2. Both panels represent the annual data from a single female bighorn sheep that was collared in association with our mountain ungulate research in the Greater Yellowstone Area. The winter range (blue), spring migration (green), summer range (red), and fall migration (yellow) are shown as a map in the top panel. The lower panel shows the distance of each GPS location to the winter range. Figure by Blake Lowrey, Montana State University.*

traced her spring migration route over the course of 10-day period, arriving back on winter range on October 20th.

In addition to plotting the points on a map, biologists can use other metrics to help define the migratory periods. For example, Figure 2 shows the straight-line distance from each successive GPS location back to the winter range. This distance remains small while an animal inhabits the winter range but begins to increase as animals move away from winter range to summer range during the spring migration. Identifying the initial changes in the distance from winter range can help to identify the start of migration. The end of migration is then noted by the leveling of the distance from winter range while on summer range. The pattern is then reversed in the fall as animals move back to winter range from summer range.

While plotting GPS data on a map is exciting, it is just the first step in beginning to identify and understand migratory behavior. Additional analyses can provide detailed maps of migratory corridors and stopover sites, identify possible drivers of migration, or assess the factors that influence migration timing or migratory diversity. Importantly, maps and other visuals can help to identify possible threats to migratory routes such as fences, roads, or other infrastructure and help direct management and conservation efforts.

*A collared mountain goat in the Snake River Canyon of Wyoming fitted with a larger GPS collar to collect detailed movement information for a few years, and a smaller VHF collar to allow monitoring of this animal's survival over its lifetime. Photo by Mark Gocke, Wyoming Game and Fish Department.*

*Bacterial mat in a Yellowstone hot spring. Microscopic organisms in Yellowstone hot springs, called thermophiles, facilitated the genomic revolution and the use of DNA in many ways that benefit society. Photo by Sally Flesch.*

# Chapter 5
# Genetic Attributes and Research Interests

*Elizabeth P. Flesch, Tabitha A. Graves,*
*Robert A. Garrott, Sarah R. Dewey, and Carson J. Butler*

## THE GENOMICS REVOLUTION AND YELLOWSTONE

Genetic research and engineering have infiltrated our daily lives in countless ways. New advances due to genomics are in the news almost every day. Genomics involves identifying the structure and function of genomes, which consist of the genetic information in individuals. Prior to the 1980s, scientists had a limited ability to study genetic material called DNA, which is short for deoxyribonucleic acid. Unlike today, they could not identify criminals using forensics, diagnose certain medical conditions and inherited diseases, or genetically modify plant crops for resistance to diseases and drought. In 1985, scientists invented an approach to make many copies of a small amount of genetic material. Scientists called this replication a polymerase chain reaction (PCR). A microorganism, *Thermus aquaticus*, discovered in a Yellowstone hot spring, provided the critical ingredient, Taq polymerase, to make this reaction possible. Taq polymerase assists in the steps necessary to replicate DNA and can withstand the heat necessary for the procedure. Today, laboratories produce many versions of this enzyme for a wide range of studies and applications. The technology that emerged from studying a Yellowstone hot spring now helps us understand, manage, and conserve the web of life in the Yellowstone area and throughout the world.

## WHAT IS DNA AND HOW DO WILDLIFE BIOLOGISTS USE IT?

Just as in people, DNA provides the instruction book for life within bighorn sheep and mountain goats. Multiple influences on the DNA of a wildlife population, including gene flow through the movement of breeding individuals from one area to another, mutation, selection, and chance, operate on different timescales. Not only does DNA code for an individual's appearance and biological processes, but it is also the source of adaptation to specific diseases, environmental conditions, and food resources. Genetic diversity, variation in the DNA of an individual or population, provides the potential for adaptation to changing conditions, such as exposure to new diseases. Scientists study the genetics of bighorn sheep and mountain goats in the Greater Yellowstone Area to identify how past events have shaped today's populations, which can aid in future conservation and management decisions. (Carlson et al. 2014, Smith et al. 2014, Frankham et al. 2017)

To evaluate wildlife genetic information, scientists must first obtain samples that contain DNA. You can read about the types of samples that biologists collect, such as blood samples, in the "How We Learn" box. If you looked at a blood sample under a microscope, you would observe many different cells. White blood cells, which help the immune system respond to disease, contain a nucleus. The nucleus holds genetic material, called nuclear DNA, with instructions not only for the white blood cell but also for the entire organism. Each cell contains only a single copy of nuclear DNA, arranged in chromosomes that look like bundles of thread. Just as in humans, these chromosomes occur in pairs in mountain ungulates, with one chromosome from the father and one from the mother, and nuclear DNA codes for most traits of an individual, such as eye and hair color. If you looked at one strand of DNA, it would look like a ladder, with pairs of nucleotides that make up the rungs. Geneticists use different letters to represent these nucleotides (also called bases), including A for adenine, G for guanine, T for thymine, and C for cytosine. These letters are the alphabet that code for the processes that make up an organism.

Bighorn sheep and mountain goat genomes consist of about 2.9 and 2.5 billion base pairs, respectively. (*"Oreamnos americanus* (ID 17040) - Genome - NCBI" n.d., *"Ovis canadensis* (ID 10514) - Genome - NCBI" n.d.)

The nucleus is not the only place containing DNA in a cell. The mitochondria, a subcellular organelle that regulates cell energy, has its own DNA in a circular shape that is different from nuclear DNA. Mitochondrial DNA consists of about 16,000 base pairs and codes for proteins that are involved in energy metabolism. In most species mitochondrial DNA is inherited only from the mother, which means that the variation found within this type of DNA comes from mutation rather than a combination of DNA inherited from both parents. Thus, biologists can use mitochondrial DNA to track inheritance of DNA from mothers over many generations. In addition, the lower variability of mitochondrial DNA makes it useful in distinguishing genetic differences among wildlife populations and species. Because each cell has many copies of mitochondrial DNA, it is also easier to isolate than nuclear DNA in non-invasive samples that are lower in quality or not fresh. Thus, scientists can use mitochondrial DNA to track genetic information over long periods of time, such as when and where groups of humans moved out of Africa thousands of years ago. (Quintana-Murci et al. 1999, Barr et al. 2005, Olivieri et al. 2006, Frankham et al. 2010, 2017; Garrett and Grisham 2013, Davenport et al. 2018)

Although everyone has their own unique genome (except for identical twins or clones), there are many genetic similarities across people and species. Domestic sheep and humans share 76% of their genomes. When comparing the DNA of two different people, 99.9% of their genomes are the same, but the remaining 0.1% difference accounts for variability in appearance, susceptibility to diseases, and many other traits. Thus, researchers identify the limited areas (called loci) of DNA in wildlife that show differences among individuals to address research questions about their populations. In the Greater Yellowstone Area, scientists have evaluated genomes of bighorn sheep and mountain goats to understand how their populations have changed over time, determine the level of genetic differences among today's populations and individuals, and identify the origin of animals that dispersed into new areas. These research questions can help improve our understanding of the history of wildlife populations and provide information for future decisions to enhance their long-term well-being. (Poissant et al. 2010, Auton et al. 2015, "*Ovis aries* Annotation Report" 2015)

## ANCIENT AND CONTEMPORARY BIGHORN SHEEP POPULATIONS

### LEARNING ABOUT BIGHORN SHEEP FROM THOUSANDS OF YEARS AGO

Bighorn sheep have inhabited the Greater Yellowstone Area for thousands of years as a significant large herbivore (plant eater) in the ecosystem and an important food source to native people. Following European colonization across the west, market hunting and domestic sheep grazing resulted in drastic reductions in bighorn sheep populations. The Greater Yellowstone Area was no exception (see chapter 2). The 1877 Yellowstone Superintendent's report indicated several thousand bighorn sheep were removed from the area, mostly for pelts, between 1870 and 1877. This drastic reduction in the population size likely contributed to a loss of genetic diversity in the area. Superintendent Norris indicated thousands of bighorn sheep still ranged in the mountains along the eastern side of the park, but these remaining bighorn sheep were potentially impacted by exotic respiratory diseases introduced by contact with domestic sheep grazing near the park. The introduction of exotic respiratory diseases into the Greater Yellowstone Area undoubtedly resulted in catastrophic die-offs of bighorn sheep and strong selection for individuals that could mount successful immune defenses. Recent sampling of bighorn sheep populations in the region indicated these exotic pathogens are present in nearly all population segments (see chapter 6). These findings suggest current bighorn sheep populations have likely been under continuous selection pressure for resistance

*Ancient bighorn sheep skull thousands of years old. Scientists have extracted DNA from ancient bighorn sheep bones and skulls to compare the bighorn sheep of the past with today's populations. Photo by Craig Lee, University of Colorado–Boulder.*

against the exotic pathogens since domestic sheep were introduced into the area approximately 150 years ago. Genetic research can help evaluate how these past events influenced the bighorn sheep that roam the region today. (Norris 1878, Buechner 1960, Avise et al. 1988, Lee and Puseman 2017, Butler et al. 2018)

Anthropologists studying artifacts from receding ice patches in alpine areas of the Greater Yellowstone Area recovered ancient skull caps, horn cores, and bones from bighorn sheep in the northern area of the Beartooth-Absaroka Mountains. They suspect native people left bighorn sheep remains at the same site over many hundreds of human generations. Multiple bighorn sheep specimens were radiocarbon dated to 685 to 5,530 years before present. Scientists can compare DNA from these ancient samples to the genomes of today's bighorn sheep by determining the order of their base pairs (A, G, T, and C), which is called sequencing.

Because ancient DNA degraded into smaller pieces over time, determining the order of the base pairs that made up the original genome is like putting together a complex jigsaw puzzle. Thus, studying mitochondrial DNA is useful in this case because it degrades less over time and there are more copies per cell than nuclear DNA. In addition, the smaller size of mitochondrial DNA makes it easier for geneticists to reconstruct, as there are fewer puzzle pieces that need to be put together to rebuild the full mitochondrial genome. Scientists expect the genome of the pre-settlement bighorn sheep to represent the historic condition of native bighorn sheep when their populations were numerous and free of diseases introduced by domestic sheep. This approach can help us determine how the population inhabiting the Beartooth-Absaroka Mountains has changed over thousands of years.

Researchers plan to compare 26 mitochondrial DNA genomes from contemporary bighorn sheep in the Beartooth-Absaroka Mountains with six ancient samples by constructing a phylogenetic tree. Like a family tree, which shows how individuals are related by birth, a phylogenetic tree shows how ancient and contemporary animals are similar based on their DNA sequences. Using this information, scientists plan to evaluate both how market hunting and domestic sheep diseases influenced the bighorn sheep population. In addition, recall that mitochondrial DNA is only inherited from the mother, and bighorn sheep groups of mothers and daughters maintain a similar home range (geographic area where they live) over multiple generations. Thus, scientists also can evaluate how stability of ewe home ranges might affect how bighorn sheep are related across geography over thousands of years. This effort represents an exciting and unique opportunity to help us understand the relatively rare, but important, process of female dispersal across time. (Hunter and Milner 1963, Geist 1971, Avise 2000, Nei and Kumar 2000, Fisher and Matthews 2001, Frankham et al. 2010)

## Evaluating genetic differences between today's bighorn sheep herds

Following the loss of many bighorn sheep populations across the West, wildlife managers relocated more than 21,500 bighorn sheep in over 1,460 translocations across many states to start new herds and supplement existing herds. As a result, today's populations originated in one of three ways: reintroduced herds started by animals from distant sources; native herds supplemented with animals from other areas; and native herds that did not receive additional animals from other populations. It is not always clear which animals survived and reproduced after many of the attempted translocations. If we knew which translocations were successful, and how this depended on the environment where the source herd came from, we could improve the success of future translocations. Genetics can help us understand how bighorn sheep populations are related and inform future translocation planning. (Wild Sheep Working Group 2015)

To account for male genetic contributions and obtain more detailed information than what mitochondrial DNA can provide, researchers studied nuclear DNA from populations of bighorn sheep. The nuclear genome is much larger than the mitochondrial genome and sequencing many animals requires considerable resources and laboratory effort. To optimize the efficiency of nuclear DNA research, scientists employed a different approach that targets only the variable areas of DNA, capitalizing on the fact that most of the genome is similar between two individuals. One specific location, where the nucleotides forming the "rungs" of the DNA ladder commonly vary, is a single nucleotide polymorphism or SNP (pronounced "snip"). For example, at the same place in a DNA strand, one bighorn sheep may have a C (cytosine), whereas another may have a T (thymine). This difference may be functional, contributing to one individual having darker fur than another, or may be neutral, meaning that the difference has no effect that scientists have detected yet. In the human genome, one SNP occurs on average every

1,000 nucleotides, meaning that each person has about 4 to 5 million SNP sites. Scientists can target specific locations in the bighorn sheep genome where the nucleotide tends to vary by using a SNP chip. A SNP chip is a slide that holds short DNA sequences that attach to portions of the DNA that contain a SNP, enabling a laboratory machine to identify which nucleotide is found at the SNP site. Researchers developed an Ovine High Density SNP chip to evaluate domestic sheep that contains over 600,000 different SNPs found at known locations throughout the genome. Bighorn sheep and domestic sheep diverged as separate species from a common ancestor about three million years ago. These two species can interbreed and produce viable offspring, and still have the same number of chromosomes. Thus, the SNP chip developed for domestic sheep is also useful for bighorn sheep and contains about 24,000 SNPs that are informative for wild sheep. ( Young and Manville 1960, Avise 2004, Bunch et al. 2006, Kim and Misra 2007, Poissant et al. 2010, Miller et al. 2015, Reference 2019)

Prior to evaluating genetic differences among herds using the SNP chip, scientists developed hypotheses describing what they expected to find. Both movement of males among herds due to geographic proximity and movement of animals to new areas via translocations by wildlife managers could increase genetic similarities among populations. Researchers predicted that bighorn sheep herds near one another or with shared translocation histories would have similar genomics. However, the degree of genetic similarity could vary depending on landscape features for natural movement of animals and if animals survived and bred after managers released them for translocations. To address this hypothesis, scientists summarized variation of SNPs into a graph using a technique called principle component analysis (PCA). Scientists discovered they could detect genetic differences among bighorn sheep populations using the Ovine High Density SNP chip. Researchers compared bighorn sheep from the Taylor Hilgard population on the west side of the Greater Yellowstone Area that had a history of multiple translocations with bighorn sheep from the Beartooth-Absaroka population on the east side of the Greater Yellowstone Area that had no history of translocations from distant herds. These two populations differed genetically from one another, suggesting there has not been recent movement of breeding animals between these two areas. However, the Taylor Hilgard and Beartooth-Absaroka populations were genetically more similar to one another than the bighorn sheep population found in Glacier National Park on the United States-Canadian border, suggesting the Glacier population has been genetically separated from the other two populations for a longer period. These findings are like the large genetic differences detected by researchers in grizzly bear populations found in the Greater Yellowstone Area compared to those in Glacier National Park. Identifying how neighboring populations are genetically distinct can also be useful in identifying individuals that are descendants of translocations. For example, geneticists can

*Bighorn sheep in Glacier National Park were found to be genetically different than those in the Greater Yellowstone Area. Photo by Elizabeth Flesch, Montana State University*

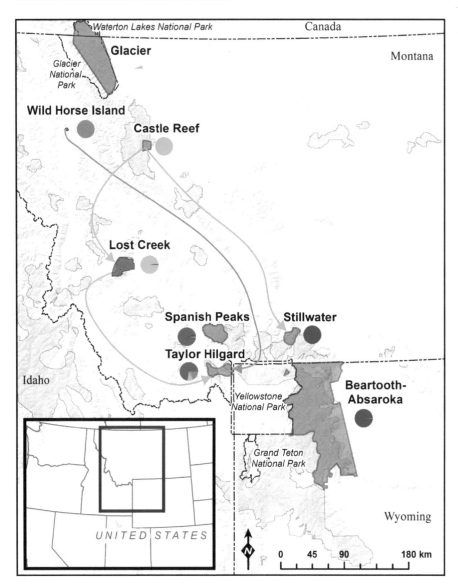

*Figure 1. Genetic analyses revealed relationships among bighorn sheep individuals and populations in the Greater Yellowstone Area due to natural and human influences. Approximate range of evaluated bighorn sheep herds are shown in brown (native herds) and dark gray (reintroduced herds). Each pie chart represents the estimated ancestry for that population based on a STRUCTURE analysis. Herd pie charts containing the same color show genetic connections due to natural movement of animals or translocations by managers (symbolized by arrows). Estimated range of bighorn sheep herds not included in this analysis are shown in gray polygons. Map by Elizabeth Flesch, Montana State University.*

determine whether translocations of male or female bighorn sheep made a larger genetic contribution to the recipient herd. This information can help inform and improve future translocation efforts that may seek to augment herd genetic diversity. (Reich et al. 2008, Haroldson et al. 2010, Francois et al. 2010, Flesch et al. 2018)

To evaluate the success of past translocation efforts in the Greater Yellowstone Area, scientists identified genetically distinct populations. A pie chart composed of two or more colors indicates the population had mixed ancestry from different sources (Figure 1). The analysis, performed using a classification approach called STRUCTURE, indicated there is some genetic connectivity between native herds in the Stillwater and Beartooth-Absaroka areas on the east side of the Greater Yellowstone Area. On the west side, the native Spanish Peaks and Taylor Hilgard herds, which are in geographic proximity, showed genetic connectivity. No genetic connections occurred between herds in geographically distant Glacier National Park and the Greater Yellowstone Area. Both Taylor Hilgard and Stillwater received translocations of bighorn sheep, implemented to enhance bighorn sheep conservation, from other areas in the state of Montana. Some of the animals transported from Lost Creek and Wild Horse Island to Taylor Hilgard made a genetic contribution (bred successfully in the new area), as their genetic influences on today's Taylor Hilgard population were detected by the analysis and represented by the source's population color. In contrast, a translocation from Castle Reef to Stillwater did not appear to make a genetic contribution, as the genetic signature of the Castle Reef population, symbolized by a different color, was not detected in the Stillwater population. The two translocations received by Taylor Hilgard were composed of 18 to 26 animals, including males and females, whereas the translocation received by the Stillwater herd included only two rams. Thus, based on the information from these translocations, scientists suspect that releasing a larger number of animals composed of males and females was more effective in genetically contributing to the recipient herd than releasing a small number of rams. (Pritchard et al. 2000, Montana Fish, Wildlife and Parks 2010, Raj et al. 2014, Flesch et al. 2020)

## DETERMINING HOW INDIVIDUALS ARE RELATED WITHIN BIGHORN SHEEP HERDS

Scientists can also use the SNP chip to evaluate genetic diversity and determine how individuals within a bighorn sheep herd are related. Large, connected populations usually have high genetic diversity and potential to adapt to new environmental conditions. Conversely, a population is at risk for inbreeding depression if it is small and does not have gene flow, with potential parents moving in from other areas, over multiple generations. Inbreeding depression describes a phenomenon where close relatives breeding with one another results in reduced reproduction or survival at the individual and population level, through mechanisms such as reduced pregnancy rates and increased disease susceptibility. This negative impact on survival and reproduction can increase the risk of the population dying out. Genetic research can help identify populations where inbreeding may be a concern, and managers may choose to intervene by connecting areas of fragmented habitat or bringing unrelated individuals into the population through translocation. (Saccheri et al. 1998, Frankham et al. 2010, 2017)

To help determine if there is inbreeding in populations that are small and isolated, scientists calculate mean kinship. Kinship measures the level of genetic similarity between two individuals. It is used, for example, to determine optimal breeding pairs for captive wildlife in zoos to minimize inbreeding. Kinship also represents the probability that the two nucleotides drawn at random from two individuals will be the same, due to a recent shared ancestor. Thus, the value of kinship represents the level of inbreeding of any offspring born from breeding the two compared individuals. For example, a mother and daughter bighorn sheep would have kinship at the level of about 0.25, as the daughter inherited 50% of the mother's DNA. Biologists can use the average of the kinship values for animals sampled from a herd to determine how related everyone is to one another, called mean kinship. A large, randomly breeding population would have a mean kinship value near zero. (Frankham et al. 2017)

*Bighorn sheep on Specimen Ridge in Yellowstone National Park. Photo by Elizabeth Flesch, Montana State University. .*

Researchers sought to predict the level of mean kinship observed for different herds based on their origin and history, as many influences in the past can affect how related individuals currently are. First, scientists expected native and reintroduced herds to have different mean kinship because initial genetic composition and diversity of founders of a newly established herd can have a strong impact on the population's genetics. When a herd is founded by a small number of individuals, it could have low genetic diversity. In contrast, native herds are more likely to contain more genetic diversity. Second, population size could affect herd genetics. Small population size can increase inbreeding due to low availability of unrelated, potential mates. Third, past bottlenecks of severe reductions in population size could also result in a loss of genetic variation. Finally, connectivity with other bighorn sheep herds is important to consider, as isolation and consequent lack of gene flow can cause a decline in genetic diversity. Thus, researchers summarized all these herd attributes to predict what the genetic information would show. The Beartooth-Absaroka is a native, large herd with high genetic connectivity across the mountain range and little potential for past bottlenecks. The Taylor Hilgard is a native, small herd with a past bottleneck due to a disease die-off and little to no connectivity with other herds. Thus, biologists predicted the Beartooth-Absaroka population would have lower mean kinship than Taylor Hilgard herd. (Nei et al. 1975, Fitzsimmons et al. 1997, Hedrick et al. 2001, Reed and Frankham 2003, Epps et al. 2005, Frankham 2007, Olson et al. 2013, Love Stowell et al. 2020)

Using genetic information for each of the herds generated using the Ovine SNP chip, geneticists determined the mean kinship values were consistent with their expectations. Bighorn sheep in the Beartooth-Absaroka herd were not very related, with a mean kinship value near zero. In contrast, the Taylor Hilgard had a higher mean kinship of 0.064, which was consistent with the herd's history, but still low and not concerning for population management. However, there can be multiple causes and interpretations of mean kinship values and evaluating these values alone cannot definitively determine if a herd is experiencing problematic levels of inbreeding. In general, mean kinship serves as a helpful piece of information to consider along with other factors to evaluate herd health. Scientists quantified mean kinship of bighorn sheep to explore the differences in genetic diversity among herds due to differing herd histories, and future research could evaluate the relationship between mean kinship within herds and population growth. (Waples 2015, Flesch et al. 2018)

## MOUNTAIN GOAT GENETIC RESEARCH

Mountain goats in and near Yellowstone National Park are not native to the area. A total of 170 mountain goats were released in the Greater Yellowstone Area at seven locations north of Yellowstone National Park in Montana in the late 1940s and early 1950s, and at two locations southwest of Grand Teton National Park in Idaho in the late 1960s and 1970s. At each location, managers introduced 5 to 33 mountain goats. When populations originate from only a few individuals, limited genetic variation exists in the new population, and variation is lower than the source population. Usually, only some animals successfully reproduce, which can further reduce genetic variation. Geneticists refer to this loss of genetic variation in small populations due to chance as genetic drift. The relatively fast differentiation helps researchers evaluate whether substantial gene flow, and thus movement, recently occurred among herds. In addition, because some genetics are still shared with the original source herd, genetics can also be used to track the origin of animals. (Frankham et al. 2010, Flesch et al. 2016)

*Teton mountain range. Photo by Elizabeth Flesch., Montana State University*

Biologists can use a part of the DNA called microsatellites to assess movements and isolation among groups of mountain ungulates. Microsatellites consist of short sequences of 1 to 5 nucleotides that repeat, such as AT AT AT. They are on chromosomes between the parts of the genome that code for traits such as hair color. Geneticists call the number of repeats at that location (locus) an allele. When DNA replication occurs, sometimes a copy of the repeating sequence (AT) is accidentally inserted or deleted on the new DNA strand, which leads to fewer or more repeats. Because they are non-coding (neutral) loci, mutations can occur in these loci without affecting the survival of the animal. At each locus, many different alleles (numbers of repeats) are possible. Thus, biologists can use microsatellites from a group of animals to detect genetic drift within a population and movements between populations. When no movements occur between groups, scientists predict that each group will have a distinct pattern of alleles. When an individual has alleles atypical for the group of animals where it was found, the individual or close relative of the individual may have moved from a different group of animals. As microsatellites are found throughout nuclear genomes of plants and animals and on mitochondrial DNA in animals, they can be used to understand the movement of both males and females, only females, or only males, depending on which microsatellite locus is studied. (Hamada et al. 1984, Weber and Wong 1993, Lunt et al. 1998, Avise 2004, Frankham et al. 2010)

Some microsatellite laboratory processes only provide information regarding the number of repeats found at the microsatellite site. Newer laboratory approaches sequence the nucleotides in the DNA using more automated processes, which provides improved certainty, objectivity, and speed. However, approaches that sequence tens to hundreds of thousands of loci, such as the SNP chip discussed above, provide more power to detect variation among individuals. The high rate of mutation in microsatellites also means that some alleles of the same length may have evolved independently in different groups of animals, which can sometimes cause confusion in studies evaluating which groups are isolated from each other. Nonetheless, because geneticists can identify microsatellites from samples with degraded or little DNA, such as hair and fecal pellets, they can be useful for non-invasive sampling. (Balloux and Lugon-Moulin 2002)

## USING GENETICS TO ASSESS ISOLATION AND SOURCE OF NON-NATIVE MOUNTAIN GOATS IN GRAND TETON NATIONAL PARK

Managers in Grand Teton National Park have been concerned about the effect of non-native mountain goats on the small, isolated bighorn sheep population in the Tetons. The first observations of solitary, likely transient, mountain goats in the Teton Range occurred in the late 1970s. Sporadic sightings of goats occurred through the 1980s and 1990s, including some of nannies with kids, but a population was not established. People observed a nanny and kid near the Grand Targhee ski resort in 2005, after which observations of mountain goats in the Tetons became more frequent. In December 2018, managers observed 88 mountain goats during a winter helicopter survey. As managers considered whether a removal program of the non-native mountain goats would be successful, they asked questions about the isolation and source of the mountain goats in the Teton Range.

The nearest mountain goat population is in the Snake River Range, southwest of the Tetons. The population originated from the introduction of 12 goats during 1969 to 1971 near Palisades, Idaho, that subsequently expanded 19 to 25 miles (30 to 40 kilometers) east into Wyoming. Most mountain goats in the Snake River Range are over 25 miles (40 kilometers) from the core range of mountain goats in the Teton Range, but in recent years, people have observed one billy and a few other scattered goats in the Snake River Range only 12 to 25 miles (20 to 40 kilometers) away from Teton Range goats. Concurrently, the closest mountain goat populations to the north, about 62 miles (100 kilometers) away, have expanded across the Beartooth and Absaroka Mountains. The nearest native goats to the Tetons are about 106 miles (170 kilometers) northwest in the Lemhi Range and Lima Peaks in Idaho and Montana. (Hayden 1984, Flesch et al. 2016)

To evaluate the likely source herd and assess recent gene flow with neighboring populations, biologists genotyped samples from 30 mountain goats captured in the Snake River Range, 28 in the Beartooth-Absaroka Mountains, and 13 in the Teton Range. They supplemented this with 34 fecal samples from the Teton Range in 2017. This resulted in 11 loci microsatellite-genotypes of 27 goats (13 males, 14 females) from the Snake River, 27 goats (9 males, 18 females) from the Beartooth-Absaroka Mountains, and 29 goats (12 males, 17 females) from the Teton Range. Three classification approaches, including PCA and STRUCTURE analyses, analogous to those applied to evaluate bighorn sheep populations, supported that the three areas are composed of three genetically distinct populations. Mountain goats in the Teton Range are genetically more similar to those in the Snake River Range than those in the Beartooth-Absaroka (Figure 2). In addition, genetic variation patterns and the presence of many private alleles found only in one area suggest the Beartooth-Absaroka population of mountain goats has multiple distinct subgroups.

Together, these analyses support the hypothesis that the most likely source of mountain goats in the Teton Range is the Snake River population and that migration between the three populations has not been common in recent generations. However, researchers may not have detected very recent movements because they did not have genotypes from all individuals in the Teton Range. Because the analysis also indicated potential substructure or variation within the Beartooth-Absaroka, scientists have limited confidence they have sufficiently characterized the genetic structure of that population. Researchers also do not have samples from a non-native herd about 73 miles (117 kilometers) away in the southern portion of the Madison Valley, Montana. Biologists need to conduct additional sampling to characterize the patterns of gene flow and genetic drift among those herds and more fully search for very recent movements.

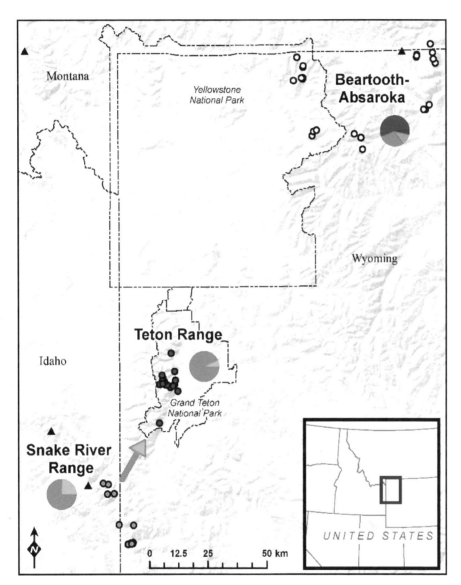

*Figure 2. This map illustrates a microsatellite locus where allele frequencies are more similar for mountain goats in the Teton and Snake River Range than those in the Beartooth-Absaroka. Each color in a pie chart represents the frequency of alleles found at that locus for each population. The blue and green arrow indicates the likely dispersal direction of mountain goats given their genetic similarity and history. Points indicate locations where mountain goat genetic samples were obtained; black triangles indicate historic locations where mountain goats were released. Map by Elizabeth Flesch, Montana State University.*

## CONCLUSIONS

Efforts to study the DNA of bighorn sheep and mountain goats in the Greater Yellowstone Area have helped illuminate how past events shaped today's populations, which can aid future conservation and management decisions. Comparing the mitochondrial genomes of ancient and contemporary bighorn sheep can provide information regarding how the population changed over time due to natural and human influences. Genetic similarities between domestic sheep and bighorn sheep allowed for an in-depth study of today's bighorn sheep genomes, including identifying how populations in different regions are related and determining which translocated animals were successful in breeding at their new location. History of disease die-offs or small population size can affect how related individuals in the same herd are to one another, and researchers can assess the potential for a harmful level of inbreeding by calculating mean kinship using genomic data. Future work can explore if existing levels of inbreeding in bighorn sheep populations have influenced population growth and recruitment of young animals into the herd. Disease can also serve as an important influence on bighorn sheep population dynamics. Because the natural selection process has been ongoing since the introduction of exotic diseases, bighorn sheep herds may have evolved to be more resilient to the pathogens through a stronger immune response or some other mechanism that may be at least partially determined by genetics. Exploration of genetic differences that could affect individual immune system response may be able to improve understanding and management of this issue. Genetic research regarding mountain goats revealed similarities and differences among geographically disparate, introduced populations and identified the most likely source of dispersing animals that founded the population in Grand Teton National Park. These efforts can serve to inform decisions regarding the conservation of mountain ungulate populations in the Greater Yellowstone Area. Genomic research will likely become an increasingly valuable tool to enhance our understanding of the natural world and ourselves.

*A group of bighorn sheep feeding in winter. Photo by Mark Gocke.*

## How We Learn: Obtaining DNA Samples for Wildlife Genomics Studies

To study the genetics of bighorn sheep and mountain goats, biologists collect blood, ear punches, tissue, and fecal pellets. Biologists label each sample with the animal's identification, location, date of sample, sex, and age (if known). When biologists capture an animal for sampling, they can safely collect a blood sample from a vein using a needle and syringe, in the same way that people have blood drawn for testing. Alternatively, biologists can place a few drops of whole blood onto a gene card, a paper treated with chemicals that stabilize DNA, for storage at room temperature for long periods. Biologists also collect ear punches with high quality DNA by punching a small hole in the ear with a sterile biopsy tool prior to ear tagging. In addition, scientists can extract DNA from muscle and lung tissue from animals harvested by hunters or killed by vehicles. Biologists can also obtain DNA by collecting fecal pellets or hair that animals have left behind, using a non-invasive collection approach. For example, researchers have placed barbed wire on rub trees and corrals of wire around scent lures to collect samples of hair from grizzly bears. Usually, less DNA is present in such non-invasively collected samples because DNA breaks down in sunlight. After researchers have collected samples, they extract the DNA from the sample in a laboratory.

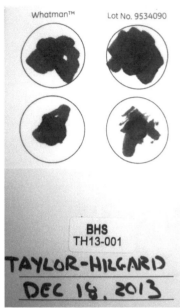

*Biologists collecting genetic samples from blood (upper left), which is put on a gene card (upper right), ear punches (lower left), and fecal pellets (lower middle).*
*Biologist checking the quality of a bighorn sheep DNA sample in a laboratory at Montana State University (lower right). Photos by Elizabeth Flesch*
*(upper left and right, lower left), Adrian Sanchez Gonzalez (lower middle), and Phil Merta (lower right) from Montana State University.*

*Bighorn sheep ram skull in a patch of heartleaf arnica. Photo by Jacob Frank, National Park Service.*

# Chapter 6
# Health and Diseases

*Mary E. Wood, Carson J. Butler, and Robert A. Garrott*

## INTRODUCTION

Bighorn sheep have been a focus of wildlife health investigations for over a century and reports of disease in bighorn sheep in the Greater Yellowstone Area date back to at least the 1880s. Many diseases have been identified and described in bighorn sheep and, to a lesser extent, mountain goats. It appears that mountain ungulates are susceptible to many of the diseases carried by domestic livestock and, in some cases, results of infection can be catastrophic. What is still poorly understood is the interaction of diseases that may have been native in mountain ungulate populations, those that were introduced through contact with domestic livestock but have attenuated over time, and those introduced by domestic livestock that still constitute a significant threat to the health and viability of mountain ungulate populations.

Despite some uncertainty regarding specific pathogens, which are agents that cause disease, most wildlife managers agree respiratory disease represents one of the most significant obstacles to bighorn sheep restoration. Outbreaks, called epizootics, occur in bighorn sheep populations with varying frequency and severity. Respiratory disease agents already present in a population can affect young lambs and the introduction of new diseases can lead to significant die-offs of animals across all ages followed by variable periods of poor lamb recruitment. Population-level responses to respiratory disease can vary dramatically from mild and sporadic, to long-term lamb losses with modest adult survival, to catastrophic all age die-offs and near population elimination.

While all-age die-offs can be highly visible and concerning, the prolonged poor lamb recruitment during or following an outbreak can be the most challenging factor to address. In some cases, poor lamb recruitment has continued in populations for decades after the initial disease event. This can lead to continually declining numbers of animals that are incapable of recruiting enough healthy lambs to support long-term population viability.

## ORIGIN AND TRANSMISSION OF RESPIRATORY DISEASE

Most respiratory disease pathogens likely originated from domestic livestock and were introduced to North America during European settlement and subsequent imports of livestock. Early reports of large bighorn sheep die-offs consistently coincided with the introduction of domestic livestock to an area. Bighorn sheep are gregarious animals with a tendency to form larger social groups. It is this social nature that sometimes draws them to domestic livestock, particularly domestic sheep, resulting in the potential for disease transmission. While these pathogens can cause significant health concerns in domestic livestock, they have likely harbored them for centuries resulting in some amount of immune tolerance over time. In contrast, mountain ungulate populations did not evolve with these livestock pathogens and appear to be very sensitive to them, particularly when new pathogen species or strains are introduced.

While pathogens were likely initially introduced into populations through contact with domestic livestock, current evidence suggests new exposures can occur from contact with both domestic livestock and other mountain ungulate populations. Therefore, wildlife managers must consider internal conservation and translocation (relocation) efforts, natural movements of wild sheep and goats, as well as proximity to domestic livestock when evaluating the causes of respiratory disease events.

## A COMPLEX HISTORY OF DISEASE

For over a century, wildlife managers have been documenting and researching disease-related die-offs in bighorn sheep populations. Many pathogens have been identified that cause respiratory disease, and new pathogens are still being identified. Thus, respiratory disease in bighorn sheep holds a complex history of continual search for the primary agents causing outbreaks, with each newly discovered pathogen bringing hope for a clearer management solution.

Early reports of die-offs in the late 1800s attributed disease and mortality to psoroptic mange, which is caused by mites (*Psoroptes ovis*) and typically associated with infestations in domestic sheep. Psoroptic mange in bighorn sheep causes crusty lesions or scabs with occasional yellowish or white discharge, mostly around the head and ears. Early reports of psoroptic mange in bighorn sheep date back to the late 1800s shortly after the arrival of domestic sheep, and this parasite is likely present to some extent in many populations in the Greater Yellowstone Area. The true population impact of psoroptic mange is unclear because disease diagnostics were limited until the late 20th century and concurrent conditions such as respiratory disease may have been under-recognized. (Honess and Frost 1942, Buechner 1960)

Starting in 1927, a new potential cause for bighorn sheep population die-offs was described when lungworm larvae were found in bighorn sheep dying of respiratory disease. Lungworm is a parasite caused by nematodes, primarily Protostrongylus, and is a native parasite of bighorn sheep. Initially, researchers speculated lungworm infestations caused damage and irritation to the lungs, allowing for secondary bacterial infections resulting in pneumonia. Reports of pneumonia in bighorn sheep became more and more common through the mid-1900s. Decades of work ensued, focusing on investigation, treatment, and management of lungworm infections in bighorn sheep with limited success in the overall management of populations. Experimental infection of lambs with lungworms did not cause fatal pneumonia and lungworms also were found in apparently healthy bighorn sheep. This suggested lungworm may not be the sole agent causing respiratory disease, though it may still be a component in areas where it is prevalent. (Rush 1927, Forrester 1971, Samson et al. 1987, Muschenheim et al. 1990, Miller et al. 2000)

During the same period when research focused heavily on lungworm, some researchers began to investigate the potential role of viruses and bacteria. Work in the 1960s identified bighorn sheep exposure to common livestock respiratory viruses including bovine respiratory syncytial virus and parainfluenza 3, leading to questions about whether viruses could be the underlying cause of respiratory disease. Research into viruses in association with respiratory disease have continued over the years but, to date, investigations have failed to find a common thread in respiratory disease die-offs. (Howe et al. 1966, Parks and England 1974, Spraker et al. 1986, Miller et al. 2011, Dassanyake et al. 2013)

Research in 1962 began to suggest respiratory disease in bighorn sheep shared many similarities with shipping fever in cattle and that Pasteurella bacteria may be a primary causative agent. By the 1980s, work began to focus more on bacteria from the Pasteurellaceae family as a primary disease agent, referred to as pasteurellosis in bighorn sheep. For decades, research had identified Pasteurella bacteria in lungs of bighorn sheep dying of respiratory disease. However, investigators often considered these bacteria a secondary invader and continued searching for a primary disease agent. More research began to accumulate demonstrating consistent identification of Pasteurella bacteria in the lungs of sick sheep. In addition, the rapid disease course leading to mortality was inconsistent with lungworm infection, and experimental transmission of Pasteurella bacteria to bighorn sheep resulted in fatal pneumonia. The history of Pasteurellaceae evaluation in the face of respiratory disease is complicated by changes in the nomenclature of Pasteurella bacteria over time. While the same bacteria have been consistently identified in bighorn lungs (*Mannheimia sp.*, *Pasteurella sp.*, *Bibersteinia sp.*), the nomenclature of these bacteria has changed significantly, leading to some difficulty in tracing commonalities in bacterial agents over time. Additionally, different strains of Pasteurella bacteria have been identified, which appear to lead to a variable effect in animals. In some cases, Pasteurella bacteria were isolated from apparently healthy sheep as well as those with respiratory disease. This complicated efforts to identify a single cause since disease expression in populations seemed highly variable with no clear understanding of underlying factors that may contribute to that variability. Research began to return to earlier reports and suspicions that underlying factors including stress, parasites, nutrition, and habitat may play a role in the variation of disease outcomes associated with Pasteurella bacteria, like shipping fever in cattle. (Post 1962, Monello et al. 2001, Miller et al. 2012)

Beginning in 2008, scientists began focusing on another bacterium, *Mycoplasma ovipneumoniae*, in the respiratory disease complex. Like work on Pasteurella, this new research was a follow up of earlier work identifying Mycoplasma bacteria in bighorn sheep in 1970. Infection with Mycoplasma bacteria can cause clinical signs of respiratory disease in bighorn sheep; however, it does not consistently lead to mortality. One of the main concerns for this bacteria is its' capacity to impair an animal's ability to clear other pathogens from the respiratory tract. Researchers began to consider the potential for Mycoplasma to act as a primary infectious agent that would then make bighorn sheep more susceptible to infection with Pasteurella bacteria. A flurry of research followed with heavy focus on Mycoplasma as a primary cause of respiratory disease in bighorn sheep. Studies began to focus on the potential to identify and remove Mycoplasma-infected animals with the hope that this may prove a viable management strategy. As research on *Mycoplasma ovipneumoniae* accrued, many of the same issues that plagued Pasteurella as a primary causative agent were identified. For example, different strains of Mycoplasma bacteria appear to lead to different disease outcomes and Mycoplasma bacteria have been isolated from apparently healthy bighorn sheep and in populations without indication of clinical respiratory disease.

*Sampling a mountain goat for respiratory pathogens. This biologist is collecting a tonsil swab sample. Photo by Mark Gocke, Wyoming Game and Fish Department.*

Again, these findings complicate efforts to identify a single cause of respiratory disease in bighorn sheep. As research on *Mycoplasma ovipneumoniae* continues, more focus has been placed on understanding variations in bacterial strains that may cause some strains of Mycoplasma to be more capable of causing disease than others. (Woolf et al. 1970, Besser et al. 2008, Butler et al. 2018, Kamath et al. 2019)

Amidst the flurry of research on *Mycoplasma ovipneumoniae*, researchers in Colorado began noticing unusual changes to the sinuses of bighorn sheep culled from populations with respiratory disease. These sheep had chronic sinus infections as well as overgrowth of the sinus lining and bone. These growths, currently referred to as sinus tumors, can fill the sinuses of bighorn sheep and occasionally even erode through the skull. The tumors appear to be infectious and a viral cause is suspected; however, the definitive causative agent has yet to be identified. Sinus tumors can obstruct the sinus cavities of a bighorn sheep and may impair clearance of respiratory pathogens from the sinuses. In this way, sinus tumors appear to provide an ideal environment for bacterial proliferation as well as a mechanism for bacterial shedding and transmission. (Fox et al. 2011, 2015, 2016)

Each new discovery of a potential causative agent led to a new wave of research and debates among researchers. Significant effort was put forth to identify the single pathogen responsible for respiratory disease in mountain ungulates. What has become apparent is that each newly identified disease agent was likely additive to the disease complex rather than a replacement of agents previously identified. Ultimately, it appears respiratory disease is a complex syndrome that likely results from the convergence of numerous disease agents interacting with other ecological factors at the population level. Both respiratory disease and the pursuit to better understand its causes are ongoing.

## RESPIRATORY DISEASE – CURRENT UNDERSTANDING

Many pathogens have been implicated in bighorn sheep respiratory disease and the relative importance of each has been vigorously debated among researchers. Most researchers agree respiratory disease is characterized by multiple pathogens combined with multiple outside factors leading to variable disease expression in a population. Current research suggests the primary pathogens involved in the disease syndrome include the bacterium *Mycoplasma ovipneumoniae* and multiple species of bacteria belonging to the Pasteurellaceae family, some of which carry a toxin (leukotoxin) that attacks white blood cells. Further research indicates infectious tumors found in bighorn sheep sinuses may be a significant contributor to the respiratory disease complex by preventing normal clearance of bacterial pathogens from the sinus lining. In addition to these pathogens, other bacteria such as *Fusobacteria necrophorum*, as well as respiratory viruses including parainfluenza, bovine respiratory syncytial virus, and bovine herpesvirus-1 (infectious bovine rhinotracheitis), and parasites such as lungworm or psoroptes mites have been implicated as potential co-factors.

Data suggests some pathogens are sufficiently virulent to cause severe disease outbreaks in the absence of other ecological factors. Captive studies involving the comingling of bighorn sheep with domestic sheep consistently result in the mortality of bighorn sheep. However, the broad variability in disease outcomes among free-ranging bighorn sheep populations in the West also suggests that, in some scenarios, other factors may significantly contribute to disease outcomes at the population level. These could include ecological factors such as habitat availability and use, forage quality, trace minerals, population density and crowding, predation, translocation efforts, loss of population knowledge of optimal landscape use, as well as animal factors such as nutritional status and immune competence and responses to disease agents. These factors may be particularly important in populations in the Greater Yellowstone Area that tend to be large and robust with diverse habitat utilization, potentially resulting in more disease tolerance than smaller, transplanted populations in other areas across the West. (Besser et al. 2012b, Dassanyake et al. 2013, Fox et al. 2015, Shanthalingam et al. 2016, Butler et al. 2018)

## RESPIRATORY DISEASE IN MOUNTAIN GOATS

Most research and understanding of respiratory disease in mountain ungulates focuses on bighorn sheep; however, more recent research has begun to investigate disease in mountain goats. Most respiratory pathogens of bighorn sheep have also been documented in mountain goats including lungworm, *Mycoplasma ovipneumoniae*, multiple Pasteurella species, respiratory viruses, and sinus tumors. Population responses to these respiratory pathogens in mountain goats are less well documented than in bighorn sheep. However, clinical signs of disease and negative population impacts from these pathogens have been described in recent literature. Documentation of respiratory pathogens in mountain goat populations brings a concern for negative population impacts, as well as concern over the potential for disease transmission between bighorn sheep and mountain goats on shared ranges. (Dunbar et al. 1986, Blanchong et al. 2018, Lowrey et al. 2018a, Wolff et al. 2019)

## EPIDEMIOLOGY AND SIMILARITIES TO DOMESTIC DISEASES

Throughout the years, multiple researchers have suggested respiratory disease in bighorn sheep shares many similarities with shipping fever (also known as bovine respiratory disease) in cattle. This is a complex disease syndrome where multiple factors come together to result in respiratory disease in cattle, particularly in calves. Typically, this disease is caused by the interaction of primary stressors such as weaning, shipping, handling, and nutrition that may weaken the immune response of the animal and allow for bacteria to infect the lungs and cause pneumonia. Effective management of this syndrome in livestock includes managing stressors, reducing overcrowding, vaccination, and implementing treatment of sick animals.

It is only through this combined approach that effective management of shipping fever is achieved.

Shipping fever provides an excellent example of why we must recognize the role of multiple factors on disease expression in a population. Epidemiology is the basic study of the patterns, causes, and distribution of disease in a population. This field of study is highly valuable when trying to understand what factors affect an outbreak of disease in a population. One of the simplest epidemiology concepts is the Epidemiologic Triad, where disease expression in a population can be considered a function of the relationship between a disease agent, a host (such as an animal that can get the disease), and the environment. There are many complex interactions that can occur between an agent, host, and the environment to result in various disease outcomes within a population. To understand disease outcomes and identify potential preventative measures or management options, one must assess all three components and their interactions.

## HISTORY OF RESPIRATORY DISEASE AND OUTCOMES IN THE GREATER YELLOWSTONE AREA

The Greater Yellowstone Area holds one of the greatest remaining concentrations of bighorn sheep in the United States. As such, it may surprise many to learn the ecosystem has a long history of disease die-offs, dating back to the 1880s. By the early 20th century hundreds of thousands of domestic sheep grazed even the most remote areas. Die-offs caused by pneumonia were recorded as early as the 1920s in Yellowstone National Park and records of psoroptic mange die-offs date back to the 1880s in the Wind River Range, the Absaroka Range, and the Beartooth Range. It is plausible pneumonia also contributed to these early die-offs attributed to psoroptic mange. In the Meeteetse, Wyoming area, a disease die-off in 1880 reduced the number of bighorn sheep that could be counted in the foothills above the Greybull River from 'thousands' to several dozen in 1881. In the Gros Ventre mountain range, a pneumonia die-off reduced the number of animals counted in the area from 1,207 in 1934 to 234 in 1938. Though early records are sparse, examples such as these suggest bighorn sheep throughout the Greater Yellowstone Area suffered immense disease-related losses following the introduction of domestic sheep to the region. Despite the devastating impacts of disease, bighorn sheep populations managed to persist in many parts of the ecosystem and most contemporary populations are 'native' populations whose ancestors occupied the region for millennia and survived the introduction of non-native diseases. (Honess and Frost 1942, Buechner 1960)

Disease continues to affect bighorn sheep throughout the Greater Yellowstone Area, with a wide range of severity and outcomes. The most well-known example is the pneumonia die-off that struck the renowned Whiskey Basin population in 1991. Nearly 30 years after the all-age die-off, lamb recruitment remains well below pre die-off levels and the population is less than half of its former size. In contrast, the neighboring Jackson population, which occupies the Gros Ventre and northern Wyoming ranges, went through two pneumonia die-offs since 2000 but quickly rebounded to pre die-off levels in both cases. Like the Jackson population, the Upper Yellowstone population, which is spread throughout the upper Yellowstone River drainage in Montana and Yellowstone National Park, experiences chronic, relatively mild, pneumonia symptoms, but managed to maintain and rebound after recent disease events. In the Madison Range, the Hilgard population was nearly extirpated after a second pneumonia die-off during the severe winter of 1996-1997 left only a few dozen animals alive. However, the population rapidly recovered and grew to nearly 300 individuals by 2013. A population introduced to the lower Boulder River drainage of Montana went extinct following a pneumonia outbreak that occurred in 2000. Other populations in the Absaroka, Beartooth, Teton, and northern Madison ranges have no confirmed history of pneumonia die-offs, though it seems likely that historical die-offs occurred. Additional pneumonia die-offs have likely occurred in modern times; however, many populations occupy such remote locations that confirming pneumonia as a cause of sudden population declines is nearly impossible. For example, between 2011 and 2013 bighorn sheep counts and lamb recruitment in the southern Absaroka Range declined sharply and hikers recovered over 150 skulls of recently deceased rams in the area over multiple years. The pattern strongly suggests a pneumonia die-off occurred, but no conclusive evidence exists. Cases of pneumonia in individual animals are relatively common throughout the ecosystem. (Ryder et al. 1992, Montana Fish, Wildlife and Parks 2010, Sells et al. 2015, Butler et al. 2018)

As newcomers to the Greater Yellowstone Area, mountain goats do not have the same history of disease as bighorn sheep. The steady expansion of mountain goats across the area suggests disease is not currently having a significant impact on their populations. However, isolated cases of pneumonia mortality have been reported.

## RESPIRATORY PATHOGENS IN BIGHORN SHEEP AND MOUNTAIN GOAT POPULATIONS

The bacteria linked to pneumonia in bighorn sheep are essentially ubiquitous among bighorn sheep populations in the Greater Yellowstone Area. Pasteurella bacteria are present in all tested populations, as is *Mycoplasma ovipneumoniae* except in the Teton Range. This likely reflects a long-history of respiratory disease in the ecosystem, as well as intact historical lineages and connectivity among most remaining populations. The pathogens found in present populations may have been circulating since the arrival of domestic sheep to the ecosystem nearly 150 years ago, though it is impossible to know their origins with certainty. The same bacteria also have been found in most mountain goat populations that have been tested in the ecosystem, once again, except for the Teton Range. (Butler et al. 2018, Lowrey et al. 2018a)

The effects of respiratory pathogens can be catastrophic to bighorn sheep populations, as they were for the, now extinct, population in the Boulder River. However, the common presence of these pathogens in one of the continent's strongholds for bighorn sheep indicate populations in the Greater Yellowstone Area may possess some resiliency in the face of respiratory disease. The reasons for this resiliency are currently unknown but may be a combination of factors such as habitat availability and utilization, population size, and possibly some attenuation (or lessening of severity) of pathogens over time. Since many of the populations are large, native populations that have developed population-knowledge of the landscape over millennia, it may be that their ability to occupy a diverse range of habitats and utilize varied survival strategies is what provides them with some buffer in the face of respiratory disease.

## OTHER DISEASES AND PARASITES

While respiratory disease currently represents the most significant disease concern facing mountain ungulate populations, multiple other diseases and parasites have been identified with varying levels of impact and concern to populations. Contagious ecthyma, otherwise known as orf, sore mouth, or scab mouth, is a viral disease documented in both bighorn sheep and mountain goats. The disease results in scabby lesions primarily on the lips and muzzle, but also occasionally on the legs, feet, udder, and labia. Lesions typically heal in 1 to 2 months and animals develop some amount of immunity after infection. While contagious ecthyma does not typically result in high mortality, severe cases with significant lesions around the mouth can reduce foraging and lead to poor body condition and sporadic mortality. While some amount of contagious ecthyma is seen in mountain ungulate populations in the Greater Yellowstone Area, periodic larger outbreaks may be seen when many naïve animals are exposed to the disease. Contagious ecthyma is a zoonotic disease and humans can develop painful sores after handling affected animals. (Samuel et al. 1975)

Infectious keratoconjunctivitis or 'pink-eye' is a contagious disease affecting the eyes. The disease is associated with low mortality but can affect large numbers of animals within a population given the right conditions. Clinical signs in bighorn sheep

*Bighorn sheep ram with contagious ecthyma (sore mouth). Although deaths can be associated with this disease, animals can, and do recover. Photo by Jacob Frank, National Park Service.*

*Keratoconjunctivitis, or pinkeye, has caused the cloudy left eye of this bighorn sheep ewe. Although not fatal itself, this disease leaves animals vulnerable to predation and accidents. Photo by Doug McWhirter, Wyoming Game and Fish Department.*

have been reported as mild to severe discharge from the eyes, swelling of the eyelids, cloudy or milky eyes, and blindness in severe cases. The disease can affect either one or both eyes. An outbreak of keratoconjunctivitis associated with a *Chlamydia sp.* bacteria was reported in bighorn sheep in Yellowstone National Park in the early 1980s. The outbreak was reported to cause a die-off of approximately 60% of a population estimated at 500 bighorn sheep. While there are occasional reports of outbreaks in mountain ungulate populations, additional die-offs associated with keratoconjunctivitis have not been reported in the Greater Yellowstone Area. Sporadic cases of keratoconjunctivitis undoubtedly still occur, however, it is not currently considered a disease of significant concern at the population level. (Meagher et al. 1992)

Additional diseases have been documented in mountain ungulates; however, cases appear to be sporadic in the Greater Yellowstone Area and do not currently appear to cause significant persistent population-level impacts. These diseases include, but may not be limited to, bluetongue virus, anaplasmosis, Johne's disease, malignant catarrhal fever, bovine viral diarrhea, necrobacillosis, and a variety of internal and external parasites.

## ASSESSING NUTRITION AND PHYSIOLOGICAL STATUS

Mountain ungulates live in a seasonal environment that typically provides nutritious and abundant forage during the 5 to 6 month growing season with energy and protein in excess of what the animals need for daily body maintenance. The excess nutritional resources are converted to muscle mass and fat that are used by the animals during the remaining 6 to 7 months of the year when nearly all plants are dry and dormant and lack the nutrition to meet daily metabolic demands. The typical deep winter snows experienced in the Greater Yellowstone Area add to nutritional stress because animals must expend additional energy to move through the snow pack and uncover plants when foraging.

In a typical year, air temperatures and precipitation during the spring and summer result in a growing season that produces an adequate quantity and quality of forage for mountain ungulates to store enough body reserves to survive the prolonged period of winter shortages as well as nourish the unborn young conceived in the fall until birth in spring. Weather conditions, however, are quite variable from year-to-year and from place-to-place across the expansive landscape. Droughts, extended growing seasons due to good late summer and fall precipitation, annual differences in the duration and depth of snow, and grazing by other wildlife and livestock all impact the forage resources available to mountain ungulates. Changes to plant communities due to fire suppression, wild fires, invasive plants, and human activities and development can also influence the seasonal ranges traditionally used by mountain ungulates and the availability of resources they need to maintain health, survive, and reproduce. Hence, wildlife managers are keenly interesting in developing and employing practical techniques that can allow them to assess animal nutrition and physiological status.

One such technique to evaluate the nutritional status of a population is to utilize ultrasonography in combination with physical palpation and measurement of an animal to generate an overall body condition score and measure subcutaneous fat thickness. This information can be taken from multiple animals within a population to give an estimate of the overall nutritional condition of the population. While only providing a snapshot in time, the nutritional status of animals in a population may reflect on ecological factors influencing population dynamics such as habitat quality and forage availability on the landscape. This information may be useful when evaluating outside factors that may influence a population and its response to respiratory disease. (Cook et al. 2001, 2007)

While body condition scoring and ultrasound measurements are providing biologists insight into the nutritional status of wild ungulates in the Greater Yellowstone Area, newer techniques may provide opportunity for expanded information. Metabolomics is a relatively new field of science that holds promise to expand the

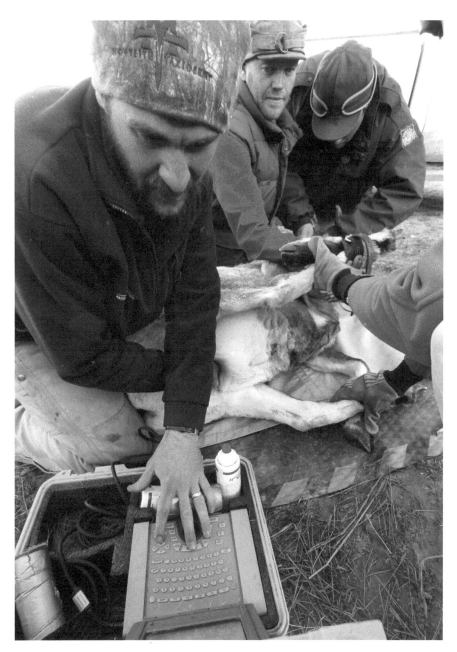

*Sampling a bighorn sheep for pregnancy using ultrasonography. Another method used to assess pregnancy is based on the presence of hormones in collected blood samples. Photo by Mark Gocke, Wyoming Game and Fish Department.*

*Nuclear magnetic resonance spectroscopy machine used to detect biological molecules (metabolites) in blood samples that may hold promise as a technique to assess the nutritional and health status of animals. Photo by Bob Garrott, Montana State University.*

ability of veterinarians, managers, and researchers to characterize the health and physiological status of wild animals. Metabolomics identifies and measures the quantities of metabolites, which are biological molecules, that represent intermediate and end products of the myriad complex biochemical processes that occur inside cells that support life. This rapidly expanding research field may better explain the functional nutritional and health states of plants and animals and is currently routinely used in the fields of human health, crop characterization, domestic livestock production, food and nutritional analyses, and environmental monitoring. Over the past five years, many hundreds of bighorn sheep and mountain goats have been captured in the Greater Yellowstone Area for ecological research. Serum extracted from blood samples obtained from these animals is being used to explore the potential of metabolomics to improve our understanding of the health and physiological status of the many populations managed by state and federal agencies in the area.

## HOW WE LEARN: HEALTH AND DISEASES

Wildlife managers, veterinarians, and researchers collect samples and take measurements from mountain ungulates to test for disease agents and evaluate their general health and nutritional status. Samples collected may vary depending upon funding, research interests, and availability of diagnostic testing. Commonly collected samples and measurements may include feces to evaluate for parasites; nasal and tonsil or oropharyngeal swabs to test for bacterial pathogens; blood to test for exposure to viruses, evaluate trace minerals, look at white blood cells, and obtain DNA for genetics; ear swabs to check for mites; and ultrasound to check pregnancy status and evaluate nutritional condition.

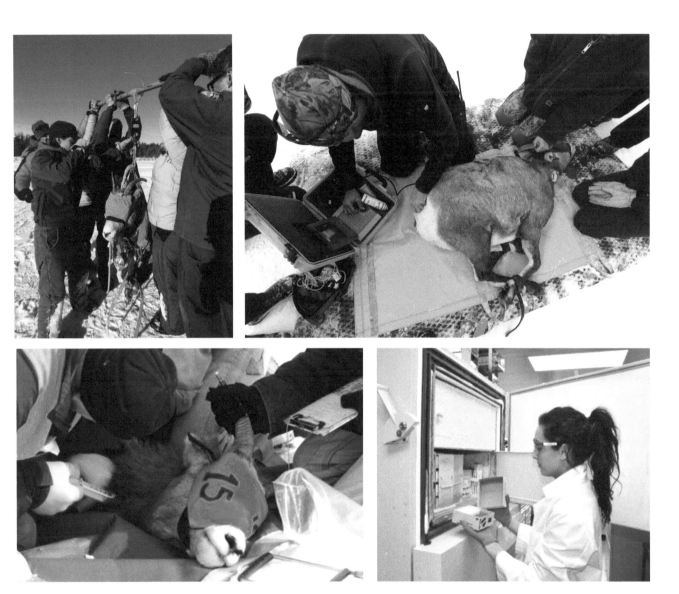

*Biologists collect samples and take measurements from mountain ungulates to test for disease agents and evaluate their general health and nutritional status.*
*Photos by Mark Gocke, Wyoming Game and Fish Department (upper left and right), Montana Fish, Wildlife and Parks (lower left), and Jim Berardinelli,*
*Montana State University (lower right).*

*A pair of bighorn sheep lambs in early winter. Photo by Mark Gocke.*

# Chapter 7
# Population Dynamics

*Robert A. Garrott, Douglas E. McWhirter,*
*Kelly M. Proffitt, Jay J. Rotella, and Kevin Monteith*

## INTRODUCTION

When you see wildlife in a natural environment such as an alpine meadow, you notice and appreciate the individual animals, their physical characteristics and behavior, whether they are alone or in a group, how they interact with others, and so on. In short, you are conscious of, and value, animals as individuals. Except for extremely rare species, which may number only in the tens or hundreds of individuals, conservation and management focuses on populations, which are aggregations of freely interacting individuals of the same species occupying a defined area at the same point in time. When there are isolated aggregations of animals occupying a distinct portion of the landscape it is relatively easy to define the distribution of the animals that make up that population. Such is the case for the Spanish Peaks bighorn population found in the northern portion of the Madison Range in the western portion of the Greater Yellowstone Area, as well as the bighorn population found in the Teton Range of Grand Teton National Park. However, when animals occur over a large landscape because of the routine seasonal movements to access disparate ranges, defining populations becomes more difficult. For example, mountain goats found throughout the northern portion of the Greater Yellowstone Area, as well as bighorn sheep distributed from the Beartooth Range in Montana all the way south along the Absaroka Range in Wyoming adjacent to the eastern boundary of

Yellowstone National Park (Figure 1). Despite the difficulty of defining populations, it is important because effectiveness of conservation and management is evaluated at the population level where agencies with administrative responsibilities routinely conduct surveys to collect data on abundance and other demographic attributes of the population. These surveys are generally conducted over a fixed area that is practical to survey and is the biologist's best estimate of the landscape occupied by an aggregation of freely interacting individuals. Surveys are performed to answer the fundamental question of 'how well are they doing', this is, are the number of animals within the survey area stable, increasing, or decreasing. If the trend in abundance is not meeting conservation or management objectives then the important question is why? For populations that are relatively isolated from one another biologists can focus on assessing reproduction and survival in an attempt to ferret out the underlying mechanisms driving the trend. When animals are more broadly distributed and split into multiple population units, the sleuthing for underlying mechanisms becomes more challenging as movements of animals among adjacent areas also may come into play.

Studies of seasonal movements of bighorn sheep and mountain goats in these areas (see chapter 4) indicate animals within localized regions interact more freely than animals in more distant locales, resulting in population substructure called a metapopulation, or what might be considered an interacting set of subpopulations. These subpopulations experience largely independent trends in reproduction and survival, but their fates are somewhat connected because movements of some animals among subpopulations loosely link them together. From the perspective of conservation, metapopulations are more desirable than isolated populations because when local conditions result in poor reproduction and survival in one subpopulation, movements of animals from other subpopulations experiencing more favorable conditions can bolster the struggling subpopulation. Thus, metapopulations are more resilient to the vagaries of climate and nature than isolated populations and,

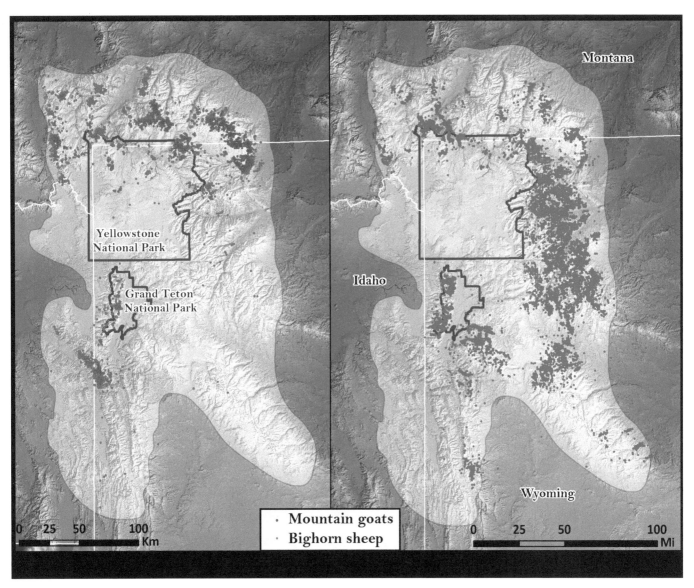

*Figure 1. The distribution of bighorn sheep (blue) and mountain goats (red) in the Greater Yellowstone Area.*
*Figure by Elizabeth Flesch, Montana State University, and colleagues (2016).*

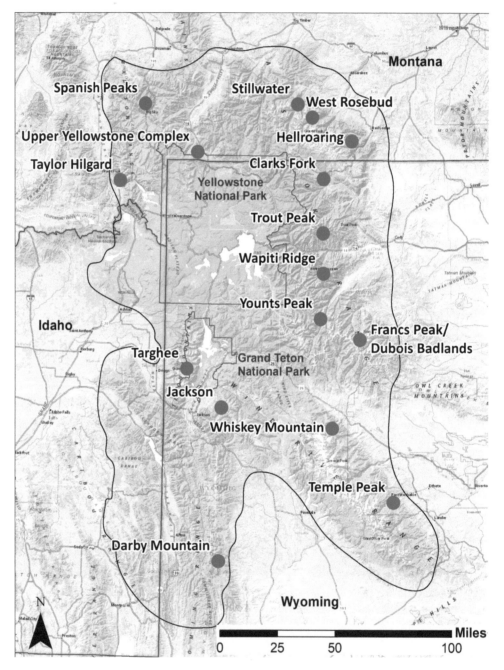

*Figure 2. Bighorn sheep population locations and names. Map by Blake Lowrey, Montana State University.*

as a result, they are less likely to undergo large changes in abundance over time. (Hanski 1999)

There are 16 recognized bighorn sheep populations distributed throughout the mountain ranges of the Greater Yellowstone Area (Figure 2). Relatively distinct and isolated populations include the Spanish Peaks and Taylor-Hilgard herds in the Madison Range, the Stillwater, Hellroaring, and West Rosebud herds in the northern Absaroka Range, Whiskey Mountain and Temple Peak herds in the Wind River Range, Jackson in the Gros Ventre Range, Targhee in the Teton Range, and Darby Mountain in the Wyoming Range. There is a large metapopulation of bighorn sheep in the eastern Absaroka Range composed of five population units, including the Clarks Fork, Trout Peak, Wapiti Ridge, Younts Peak, and Francs Peak. In addition, the Upper Yellowstone metapopulation complex is composed of about a dozen small groups of 20-80 animals that winter along the Yellowstone River and migrate into surrounding high-elevation mountainous areas during summer.

Identifying distinct mountain goat populations is difficult because they have been slowly expanding their distribution in the Greater Yellowstone Area since their introduction and there has been limited ecological research on them. Mountain goats occur throughout the Madison, Gallatin, north Absaroka, and Beartooth Ranges in Montana, as well as the northern portion of Wyoming's Absaroka Range and the Snake River Range spanning the Idaho-Wyoming border. Mountain goats have recently established a reproducing population in the Teton Range and distributions are expanding southward in Wyoming's Absaroka Range along the eastern border of Yellowstone National Park. The limited data on seasonal movements in the Greater Yellowstone Area suggest that individual mountain goats generally occupy relatively restricted home ranges; thus in those mountain ranges where mountain goats are broadly distributed we expect a metapopulation structure.

Biologists with the state and federal agencies responsible for conserving and managing these bighorn sheep and mountain goat populations conduct surveys on an annual or semiannual time frame to obtain estimates of abundance and the number of young animals added to the population. Agencies also track the location, age and sex of all harvested bighorn sheep and mountain goats. In recent years, many populations have also been incorporated into regional research projects using radio-collared adults to provide estimates of pregnancy and survival rates, as well as insights into common sources of mortality.

## REPRODUCTION

The annual cycle of reproduction is similar for bighorn sheep and mountain goats. Mature females ovulate and become receptive to mating with males in autumn. Female bighorn are typically sexually mature by the time they reach 2.5 years of age, whereas mountain goat females are slower to mature, normally breeding for the first time at 3.5 to 4.5 years of age. In general, the breeding season in the Greater Yellowstone Area for bighorn sheep and mountain goats is mid-November to mid-December, but there is some variation in the timing of the breeding season from population to population. The timing of breeding and births in populations generally is synchronized to local environmental conditions such that young are born when resources required for their successful rearing to independence are maximized. Large herbivores (plant eaters) like bighorn sheep and mountain goats time breeding such that young are born in spring when plant communities are initiating seasonal growth, which provides the most nutritious forage to support nursing and maximize the time young have access to high-quality forage after weaning and prior to the onset of winter. There is considerable variability in the timing of the growing season for plants across the Greater Yellowstone Area depending on the elevation of bighorn sheep and mountain goat spring and summer ranges. A good example of synchronization of the breeding season to local environmental conditions is the Stillwater bighorn sheep herd that summers on the high-elevation Beartooth Plateau in the northeastern portion of the Greater Yellowstone Area. These animals breed approximately one month later than what is typical for most bighorn populations in the area such that lambing occurs in late June to early July. In contrast, bighorn living 200 miles north of the Stillwater herd in the low-elevation prairies associated with the Missouri River in eastern Montana breed two months earlier, lambing in late-April to early May. (Geist 1971, Stewart 1982, Festa-Bianchet and Côte 2008)

When bighorn sheep and mountain goats breed in late-fall, they are in their peak body condition. They have recovered from the nutritional stress incurred during the winter by foraging on nutritious green vegetation throughout the spring and summer growing season and have increased substantially in weight by converting the energy and protein of the plants they have consumed into both muscle mass and fat. Growing season conditions on summer ranges in the Greater Yellowstone Area are normally sufficient for females to accrue adequate body fat during the summer to sustain a pregnancy the next fall, winter and spring. Extensive testing of mature bighorn sheep females captured for research indicates that typical annual pregnancy rates for most herds in this area are high, ranging from 87 to 95%. However, annual variation in weather can result in considerable year-to-year variation in the growing season and available forage resources. After severe winters, deep snow can persist up to a month longer in the spring than average, resulting in a delay in the initiation of the growing season. Likewise, the duration of the growing season can vary annually, with hot dry summers resulting in relatively short growing seasons and cooler wetter summers extending the growing season into the fall. The plants that bighorn sheep and mountain goats consume yield the most energy and protein when they are green and growing, so annual variation in length of the growing season due to the capriciousness of weather conditions can affect the amount of nutrition available and the muscle and fat that animals can accrue over summer. In years when the growing season is abbreviated, some females may not attain adequate body condition by fall to ovulate and breed. Indeed, bighorn herds throughout the Greater Yellowstone Area show evidence of poor years in forage conditions with pregnancy rates declining

*A nanny-kid group of mountain goats on the Beartooth Plateau. The body condition of females determines pregnancy, and combined with weather, disease, and predation determine the productivity of a population. Photo by Mark Gocke.*

to as low as 42 to 80%. Although data on pregnancy rates of mountain goats for populations in the Greater Yellowstone Area are not available, intensive studies of a Canadian mountain goat population suggest a similar range in annual pregnancy rates as that documented for bighorn sheep (Festa-Bianchet and Côte 2008)

As breeding season begins, mature males of both species, which have been generally on their own throughout the summer, join the nursery groups of females, young of year, and immature males. Both bighorn sheep and mountain goats are polygamous, with males intensely competing with each other for opportunities to mate receptive females. In most polygamous large mammals, males tend to be larger than females, a trait that likely evolved because of intense competition among males during the breeding season. Mature male bighorn sheep are approximately 40% larger than adult females, with adult males weighing 175 to 250 pounds (79 to 113 kilograms) compared with the typical weight of females of 130 to 190 pounds (59 to 86 kilograms). The difference in body size between the sexes is similar for mountain goats with males weighing 190 to 245 pounds (86 to 111 kilograms) while females range from 120 to 160 pounds (56 to 73 kilograms). During the breeding season, males display their bodies and horn sizes to one another during ritualized posturing behaviors with larger, older males tending to be dominant over younger, smaller males. Physical competition between males of similar size and dominance is common and on spectacular display when two large bighorn sheep rams square off a short distance from one another. They rear up on their hind legs, charge forward, and use the full weight and strength of their bodies to clash their horns together with a resounding crack that people can hear from as far as a mile away. The shock of the impact can frequently drive one of the combatants backward and sometimes damage their horns. Physical competition among mature mountain goat males is not as dramatic, likely because their thin, short, dagger-like horns could easily inflict mortal wounds. In contrast to the head-to-head confrontation of bighorn rams, competing male mountain goats stand broadside to one another, oriented head to

*Bighorn rams preparing to clash heads during the rutting season. These clashes cause horn tips to become splintered or broken, sometimes significantly (inset). Rams also use body postures and horn displays as a non-combative way to establish dominance. Photo of rams clashing by Kenneth R. Whitten; photo of ram with broken horn by Jacob Frank, National Park Service.*

rump, and use their horns to attempt to strike their opponent on the flank or rump. Serious wounds are rare, but minor punctures and slashes are common. Older males have a thick dermal shield on the rump approximately 0.6 to 0.9 inches (1.5 to 2.3 centimeters) that likely minimizes the damage caused by horning during escalated fights. (Geist 1967, 1971, Festa-Bianchet and Côte 2008)

Gestation length for both mountain goats and bighorn sheep is approximately 6 months (170 to 180 days). As date of birth nears, the female usually separates herself from her normal social group and seeks out an isolated location in rugged terrain where she will remain secluded for several days to a week after the birth. Bighorn sheep normally give birth to a single lamb, and twinning is rare. Twins are more common in mountain goats and there are occasional reports of triplets. The frequency of twinning is an index of the relative quality and quantity of forage available on the summer range. The level of nutrition a female obtains before entering winter as well as conditions experienced during the winter will influence the growth rate of the fetus, with young of both species typically weighing between 7 and 9 pounds (3.2 to 4.1 kilograms) at birth. Animals on poor quality summer or winter ranges or those that experience exceptionally severe winter conditions may give birth to underweight young that have a low probability of surviving the first few days of life. After the birthing season both bighorn sheep and mountain goats aggregate into nursery groups that can exceed 50 animals. Although young nurse through the summer, they begin eating vegetation within a week to 10 days after birth and are routinely grazing by the time they are 3 weeks old. Weaning may occur anytime between late July and September, but occasional suckling occurs through the fall and winter. There is a strong social bond between the mother and her young during the summer, but in bighorn sheep the bond weakens over the winter with lambs essentially independent by spring. In contrast, the social bond between mountain goat mothers and their young commonly extends into the second year. (Lentfer 1955, Geist 1971, Festa-Bianchet and Côte 2008)

*A mountain goat nanny and kid. Tight bonds are formed between mother and offspring, as the nanny is responsible not only for sustenance and defense, but also for showing her kid how to navigate the landscape and find foraging areas at various seasons. Photo by Mark Gocke.*

## SURVIVAL RATES AND CAUSES OF MORTALITY

Survival rate is defined as the probability that an animal alive at the start of some defined time period (normally a year) will still be alive at the end of the time period. Studies of survival rates of long-lived large mammals have documented that survival probabilities for individuals vary depending on an animal's age. Survival probability is relatively low from birth through the first year of life, increases rapidly to a maximum as animals mature and reach adult body size, and declines in the oldest age classes. One of the major mechanisms believed responsible for declining survival rates for older animals is tooth wear. Plant material is hard to digest, and large herbivores like bighorn sheep and mountain goats use their teeth to both crop plants and to chew the plant material extensively to break it into small fragments that microbes in their complex stomachs can efficiently digest. If you watch these animals going about their daily lives you will notice that much of their time is spent eating, whether they are slowly walking along an alpine meadow or grassy bench on a cliff biting off plants, or bedded and chewing a bolus of plant material they have regurgitated. Plants are abrasive because of their structure and chemical composition as well as the fine soil that clings to their surface. As a result, the constant biting and chewing wears down the sharp ridges on their teeth making them less efficient at the critical task of processing and digesting their food, thus, contributing to their physiological decline as they age. Survival rates also differ for males and females due to the differences in their behavior, body size, and demands placed on each sex for reproduction (females—gestation and lactation; males—competition for mating opportunities), with males generally having lower survival rates and shorter longevity than females. (Laws 1981)

Survival is an important attribute of wildlife populations that has a strong influence on whether or not the number of animals in a population is increasing, decreasing, or remaining stable. Adult survival can vary from one population to the next because the Greater Yellowstone Area is a large and diverse landscape with each bighorn sheep and mountain goat population occupying a somewhat different environment.

*A ram chews its cud. Chewing coarse vegetation can take its toll, and an herbivores life span is dictated by how long its teeth last. Photo by Kenneth R. Whitten.*

For example, the physical characteristics of the landscape including the geology and topography affects the mosaic of plant communities and their productivity, which of course is of fundamental importance to large herbivores. The abundance of other species of animals present in the local community can also influence competition for important resources such as forage and the risk of being killed by predators. In addition, local and regional climate conditions impact how long plants are growing and nutritious each summer and how extensive and persistent snowpack is each winter, which influences the energy required for mountain goats and bighorn sheep to access the forages they need and can also make the animals more vulnerable to predation. (Dailey and Hobbs 1989)

Trends in the abundance of bighorn sheep and mountain goat populations are particularly sensitive to the survival rates of adult females. Because of the difficulty and expense, most management agencies do not routinely measure or monitor survival rates. However, over the past decade biologists have radio-collared hundreds of female bighorn sheep (see chapter 3 and 4), which has allowed the survival rates of adult females to be estimated for nearly all the bighorn sheep populations in the Greater Yellowstone Area. This work has revealed that, on average, annual survival rates of adult females vary among populations from a low of 80% to a high of 93%. Mountain goats are one of the most challenging large mammals to capture and, as a result, researchers pooled data on the modest numbers of radio-collared males and females to obtain adequate sample sizes for estimating survival rates. This research, concentrated in the Snake River Range in the southwestern Greater Yellowstone Area and the Beartooth-Absaroka region of the northeastern portion of the area, found slightly lower average annual adult mountain goat survival rates of 80% to 86%, likely due to the inclusion of males which tend to have lower survival rates than females. (Proffitt et al. 2021)

As with nearly all wildlife species, many factors can result in the death of an animal; bighorn sheep and mountain goats are no exception. The Greater Yellowstone Area has the full complement of predators that were present at the time Euro-Americans first explored the region. Mountain lions, wolves, grizzly bears, black bears, and coyotes are the most abundant predators capable of killing bighorn sheep and mountain goats and records from regional studies of these predators have documented kills of both mountain ungulates. It is also likely that golden eagles are effective predators of lambs and kids. Observations of nursery groups of bighorn sheep and mountain goats fleeing to seek shelter under ledges and in caves when golden eagles fly into view provide anecdotal evidence golden eagles are routinely attempting to prey on young mountain ungulates in some areas. Investigations of radio-collared animals that have died also indicate that accidents, particularly falls from cliffs and avalanches, are an important cause of mortalities. For those herds that occupy ranges bisected by roads, vehicle collisions also occasionally kill animals. As described in chapter 6, disease, particularly respiratory pneumonia likely caused by pathogens originally introduced into the wild populations by domestic animals, is common through-out the herds with some populations of bighorn sheep occasionally experiencing severe outbreaks that result in the deaths of significant numbers of animals. Long, severe winters in much of the Greater Yellowstone Area and the associated extensive snowpack reduces nutritional intake to sub-maintenance levels for many months each year. Prolonged snowpack leading to starvation, therefore, is another common source of mortality in bighorn sheep and mountain goats. Finally, outside the national parks, both mountain ungulate species are hunted, with state wildlife management agencies strictly controlling the number of hunters and generally limiting the annual harvest to approximately 2 to 4% of the estimated total population size.

## RECRUITMENT

Throughout the Greater Yellowstone Area, large numbers of newborn animals are added to mountain goat and bighorn sheep populations when females give birth

*A group of three bighorn lambs with a ewe in winter. The number of young born and their survival through their first year determines how many animals are "recruited" into the adult population. Photo by Mark Gocke.*

each spring. This annual 'birth pulse' has the potential to cause dramatic increases in size of populations. However, young animals are extremely vulnerable and in most years a large proportion of the young die before they reach their first birthday. When the young do survive until their first birthday, biologists consider them 'recruited' into the adult population. Thus, recruitment is an important attribute of bighorn sheep and mountain goat populations. Unlike adult survival rates, which are usually only estimated infrequently during research studies, biologists annually collect information on recruitment for most populations in the Greater Yellowstone Area. This is done by conducting aerial surveys to locate as many animals in a population as possible during mid- to late-winter and recording the number and sex of adults and the number of lambs or kids (young-of-the-year) observed. Because these surveys normally occur a month or more before young would reach their first birth day the data collected is biased high as additional mortalities are likely between the time of the survey and when animals become 1 year old. Biologists convert this information into a recruitment rate, reported as a ratio of young-of-the-year to adult females such as 28 lambs per 100 adult females or a proportion such as 0.28 lambs per adult female. It is difficult to distinguish the sex of adult mountain goats at the distances biologists normally are classifying the age and sex of animals during surveys. Thus, biologists often express mountain goat recruitment rates as kid to adult ratios. This important metric of population productivity incorporates aspects of both pregnancy rates, that determined the number of young born, and the survival rates of those vulnerable young animals into an index of the number of new animals that survive to be successfully recruited into the adult population. (Gaillard et al. 2000, Skalski et al. 2005)

In contrast with adult survival rates, which tend to be high and relatively consistent from year-to-year, recruitment rates tend to be much lower with considerable variation within a population annually as well as among populations. An examination of annual recruitment rates during 2013 to 2017 for two different bighorn herds at opposite ends of the Greater Yellowstone Area illustrates this variability. The recruitment rates recorded for the upper Yellowstone bighorn complex in the northern region were 40, 38, 26, 30, and 28 lambs per 100 adult females, while the rates recorded for the Jackson bighorn herd during the same time period trended the opposite direction and were 21, 31, 36, 41, and 34 per 100 adult females. Similar annual variation is also common in mountain goat populations in the region. For example, biologists survey the Snake River Range population biennially and recruitment rates recorded for years 2004, 2006, 2008, 2010, and 2012 were 30, 19, 28, 35, and 26 kids per 100 adults. Given the high pregnancy rates of most bighorn sheep herds in the area, the lamb to adult female ratio at birth is typically about 80, indicating that at least half of the young born each year succumb to various mortality sources before reaching their first birthday, which is relatively common for mountain ungulates. Recruitment rates needed to maintain a population will depend on other demographic attributes but are most dependent on adult female survival. Under a typical range of annual adult female survival rates of 85% or better, recruitment rates less than 20 lambs per 100 adult females would likely indicate the population is declining. (Western Association of Fish and Wildlife Agencies 2015)

## DISPERSAL

While most animals born into a population remain within the natal population range, once they reach the age where they become independent of their mother, some individuals may leave and settle in a new area, a behavior known as dispersal. The factors motivating animals to disperse are not well known. It is possible that some animals just have a propensity to wander, but the most likely driver of dispersal behavior is the search for some important resource the animal needs but cannot find in adequate abundance within its local environment. As populations grow, the density of animals in a given area increases and competition for food or access to mates and potential social tension and aggression among animals increasingly crowded into a limited space can cause animals to strike out to find new areas to live. The most obvious example of dispersal by mountain ungulates in the Greater Yellowstone Area is the gradual range expansion of mountain goats following their relocation to the region. Since being introduced into just a hand full of sites in the northern mountains of the Greater Yellowstone Area in Montana in the 1940s and 1950s, populations have grown and animals have spread widely from introduction sites into surrounding areas. Mountain goats have fully occupied the northern mountains of the Greater Yellowstone Area and are now dispersing south into the northern portion of Yellowstone National Park and the Absaroka mountain chain in Wyoming. Similarly, the few mountain goats introduced into Idaho's Snake River Range in the late 1960s and early 1970s have spread throughout the Range and have dispersed northward into Wyoming's Teton Range and Grand Teton National Park (chapter 2). (Lemke 2004, Flesch et al. 2016)

In contrast, bighorn sheep do not demonstrate the same tendency to disperse. Throughout the historic range of bighorn sheep where native populations have been reduced to remnant herds or reestablished via translocations, populations tend to maintain a localized distribution even as densities increase. The history of bighorn sheep in Montana's Madison Range in the western Greater Yellowstone Area is perhaps the best example of bighorn sheep's reluctance to disperse. Historic records indicate bighorn sheep were widely distributed throughout the range, but currently only two remnant populations occupy relatively small portions of the available landscape with the Spanish Peaks herd at the northern end of the range and the Taylor-Hilgard herd at the southern end of the range. Despite increases in population size over the past several decades, the populations have demonstrated little expansion into adjacent high-quality habitat. As a consequence, as the populations grow they concentrate in higher densities on relatively small winter ranges where the entire population is more vulnerable to potential localized severe snowpack conditions, predators concentrating on bighorn sheep, and contagious diseases. Indeed, the Taylor-Hilgard herd has experienced two catastrophic pneumonia-related die-offs that reduced the population by an estimated 60-80%, once in the mid-1980s and again in the mid-1990's. This apparent reluctance of bighorn sheep to disperse has prompted the state management agency to begin trapping animals and trans-locating them into unoccupied habitat between the two populations to repopulate the entire mountain range and establish a broadly distributed metapopulation (see chapter 9). Creating a spatially-structured broadly distributed population would reduce the potential for the entire population to be impacted by deleterious factors, thus creating a more resilient population by reducing the potential for dramatic changes in abundance. (Bleich et al. 1996, Festa-Bianchet et al. 2006, Jesmer et al. 2018, Lowrey et al. 2019, Lula et al. 2020)

## ABUNDANCE AND POPULATION TRENDS

Anyone with an interest in the conservation and management of a wildlife population, whether a professional biologist, agency administrator, member of a non-government advocacy group, or simply a person that cares about the animals, wants to know how many animals are in the population and how population size has been changing through time. These two seemingly simple questions are often some of the most difficult for wildlife biologists to address. Counting wild animals in the mountainous landscapes inhabited by bighorn sheep and mountain goats is a challenging task. The animals are scattered over large complex landscapes with distributions changing dramatically over time as animals respond to seasonal changes in the quantity and quality of the plants they eat, the accumulation and melting of snowpack, interactions with predators and other animals, and a host of other factors. They tend to be in small groups that are easily hidden from an observer by rock outcrops, trees and shrubs, and the complexity of the topography. Even when standing in the open, animals can be difficult to spot from an airplane or when scanning a mountain slope with a spotting scope. One simply cannot find and count all the animals in a population. The proportion of the animals in a population that biologists detect and count varies from survey to survey and is

Table 1. Fall/winter estimates of size and trends of bighorn sheep and mountain goat populations in the Greater Yellowstone Area. Acronyms are MFWP = Montana Fish, Wildlife and Parks; NPS = National Park Service; USFS = U.S. Forest Service; WGF = Wyoming Game and Fish Department, WRR = Wind River Reservation. and YNP = Yellowstone National Park.

| Herd | Management Agencies | Population Size | Population Trend |
|---|---|---|---|
| **Bighorn Sheep** | | | |
| Spanish Peaks | MFWP, USFS | 150-200 | Stable |
| Taylor Hilgard | MFWP, USFS | 220-240 | Stable |
| Upper Yellowstone Complex | MFWP, USFS, NPS | 350-450 | Stable |
| Stillwater | MFWP, USFS | 100-120 | Increasing |
| Hellroaring | MFWP, USFS | 30-40 | Stable |
| West Rosebud | MFWP, USFS | 60-80 | Stable |
| Clarks Fork | WGF, USFS, NPS | 550 | Declining |
| Trout Peak | WGF, USFS, NPS | 675 | Declining |
| Wapiti Ridge | WGF, USFS, NPS | 800 | Stable |
| Younts Peak | WGF, USFS | 750 | Declining |
| Francs Peak/Dubois Badlands | WGF, USFS, NPS, WRR | 825 | Declining |
| Whiskey Mountain | WGF, USFS, WRR | 500 | Declining |
| Temple Peak | WGF, USFS, WRR | 75 | Stable |
| Jackson | WGF, USFS | 400 | Stable |
| Targhee | WGF, USFS, NPS | 125 | Stable |
| Darby Mountain | WGF, USFS | 75 | Stable |
| **Total** | | **5,685-5,905** | |
| **Mountain Goat** | | | |
| Madison Range | MFWP, USFS | 447-760 | Increasing |
| Gallatin Range | MFWP, USFS, NPS | 140-275 | Increasing |
| MT Absaroka | MFWP, USFS, NPS | 250-350 | Declining |
| MT Beartooth | MFWP, USFS, NPS | 240-372 | Stable |
| WY Absaroka (including YNP) | WGF, USFS, NPS | 175 | Increasing |
| WY-MT Beartooth | WGF, USFS | 75 | Stable |
| Teton Range | WGF, USFS, NPS | 50 | Declining |
| Snake River Range | WGF, IDFG, USFS | 300 | Stable |
| **Total** | | **1,677-2,357** | |

generally unknown. Intensive research studies focused on this topic, however, suggest that routine population surveys conducted under good observation conditions likely detect 60 to 80% of the animals. (Bodie et al. 1995, Gonzalez-Voyer et al. 2001, Williams et al. 2002, Rice et al. 2009)

Despite the challenges of counting mountain ungulates, agency biologists climb into planes and helicopters every year to do the best job they can to inventory populations throughout the Greater Yellowstone Area. These surveys indicate the region contains approximately 5,700 to 5,900 bighorn sheep and 1,700 to 2,400 mountain goats (Table 1). With the exception of the restored Darby Mountain and Temple Peak herds, all the bighorn sheep populations in the Greater Yellowstone Area are native. Sheep in these populations survived the period of market hunting, competition with domestic sheep that were grazed in nearly every mountain range (Figure 2, chapter 2), and disease outbreaks caused by exotic pathogens introduced by domestic sheep in the late 1800s and early 1900s.

The survival of the native bighorn sheep herds in the Greater Yellowstone Area and their subsequent recovery is a remarkable conservation success because most bighorn sheep populations in western North America were extirpated during the period of over-exploitation, which reduced the continental population from an estimated one half to one and a half million animals to less than 25,000. Over the past century concerted efforts by natural resource agencies to restore populations throughout historic range have yielded modest success as over 1,400 translocations involving 21,500 animals have increased the continental population to approximately 50,000 in 2016. Most restored populations, however, occupy restricted ranges isolated from other bighorn herds, display weak demographic performance, and consequently are relatively small. The native herds in the Greater Yellowstone Area, especially those along the eastern boundary of Yellowstone National Park in Wyoming, represent the largest continuous distribution of bighorn sheep in North America. (Seton 1929, Buechner 1960, Singer et al. 2000, Brewer et al. 2014, Wild Sheep Working Group 2015)

Most populations of bighorn sheep in the Greater Yellowstone Area, however, have experienced substantial fluctuations in numbers. Numerous pathogens associated with pneumonia are present in all the populations, and many of the bighorn sheep populations have experienced disease related die-offs of varying magnitude (see chapter 6). Most populations have recovered from disease events, although populations generally experience a period of poor lamb recruitment prior to returning to more typical recruitment. An exception to this pattern is the Whiskey Mountain metapopulation that occupies the northern Wind River Range. The major portion of the population that winters on the east side of the range represented the largest wintering concentration of bighorn sheep in the United States, but experienced a pneumonia-related die-off during the winter of 1990-1991. Lamb recruitment in this herd has been consistently poor since then, resulting in a steady decline in the population over the subsequent three decades. Unusually severe winters have also been associated with significant mortality events and temporary declines in abundance, most commonly in populations that winter at high elevations. The Stillwater bighorn herd provides another example of population fluctuations over time. This small migratory population winters along the Stillwater River, a drainage on the northern slopes of Montana's Absaroka Mountains. The population experienced a gradual decline through most of the 1980s and into the mid-1990s associated with the development of a mine within the core of the winter range. In the late 1990s, however, the trajectory of the population reversed and numbers have been increasing slowly and steadily for the past two decades.

Mountain goats have become broadly distributed and well established following introductions into mountain ranges in the northern and southwestern Greater Yellowstone Area. Mountain goat populations in the Snake River Range, along the Wyoming-Idaho border in the southwestern Greater Yellowstone Area, and the mountains spanning the northern border of Yellowstone National Park, where Montana initially introduced mountain goats, experienced decades of gradual increases in abundance as the populations became established. These populations now appear to have stabilized with some declines noted in more localized areas. In other regions of the Greater Yellowstone Area, however, mountain goat populations are increasing. Mountain goats occur throughout the Madison and Gallatin Ranges along the western border of Yellowstone National Park and populations are continuing to increase in abundance. Along the eastern border of Yellowstone National Park, mountain goats are continuing their decades-long slow range expansion southward along Wyoming's Absaroka Range with a consequent increase in abundance. Mountain goats have also recently colonized the Teton Range and Grand Teton National Park, and this small population is increasing in size.

## CONCLUSIONS

Population dynamics of mountain goats and bighorn sheep are the result of the interactions of animals' births, deaths, and movements that dictate trends in abundance and distribution of these iconic mammals across the diverse and expansive landscape of the Greater Yellowstone Area. The interactions of many factors influence these population processes, including weather, availability and quality of forage plants, predators, competition for food and space with other wildlife species, and disease. Human activities influence population processes through our direct and indirect impacts on the attributes of the landscapes that bighorn sheep and mountain goats depend on, management of other wildlife species and domestic animals that interact with these mountain ungulates, and purposeful conservation and management actions. Monitoring the many populations of bighorn sheep and mountain goats in the region by numerous state, federal, and tribal government agencies is challenging due to the remote and rugged environments that these animals occupy. Although data on pregnancy and survival rates are not always available, biologists routinely assess the abundance and recruitment of populations via surveys to count and classify (sex/age) as many animals that can be detected in the areas occupied by each population.

Bighorn sheep populations in the region have recovered from the era of overexploitation following settlement of the region by Euro-Americans, and mountain goats have become broadly distributed and well established following introductions into mountain ranges in the northern and southwestern Greater Yellowstone Area. Individual populations fluctuate over time, but biologists consider most populations healthy and stable. As would be expected with so many populations distributed across a vast landscape, some individual populations present specific conservation challenges that management agencies are addressing with strong participation from the public.

## How We Learn: Population Demographics and Trends

Wildlife managers throughout the Greater Yellowstone Area conduct and rely on counts and classifications, such as the number of bighorn sheep ewes, rams, and lambs, to monitor the demographic vigor of populations. These surveys are often conducted once or twice per season when animals are most concentrated on winter ranges. Small populations of generally less than 200 animals that spend winter in localized areas accessible from roads can be surveyed by biologists from the ground using binoculars and spotting scopes. However, many of the bighorn sheep and mountain goat populations in the region are distributed across vast areas of remote and rugged wilderness where aircraft are the only practical means of surveying the populations. Both small fixed-wing planes and helicopters are used depending on the elevations of winter ranges, distances that must be traveled, and need to fly into steep canyons. Flights can vary from 3 to more than 6 hours with aircraft routinely buffeted by strong winds, making the surveys challenging for both pilots and biologists. Poor weather conditions, limited availability of aircraft and skilled pilots, and periodic shortages of funds result in years where surveys cannot be completed; however, management agencies are committed to monitoring surveys.

In addition to the routine management surveys, intensive short-duration (3-10 years) research projects often focus on obtaining more detailed demographic insights by studying survival and reproduction, which are the major drivers of changes in the abundance of populations. Survival studies depend on the same types of radio collars used to study how animals use various habitats and migrate between seasonal ranges (see chapters 3 and 4). Built into nearly all radio collars is a motion sensing device that can detect when an animal has not moved for an extended period (6-8 hours), indicating the animal has likely died. This information is conveyed to the biologists via a distinctive change in the pattern of the transmitted radio signal, or in the case of collars that communicate with satellites, the biologist may receive an email or a cell phone text message. Determining the cause of an animal's death, however, requires finding the dead animal and carefully examining the carcass and surrounding area. In most cases, visiting the site of a mortality does not occur immediately but may be delayed by weeks or months due to a combination of rugged terrain, remoteness, seasonally swollen rivers and streams, deep snowpack, avalanche conditions, and several other factors. Typically, all a biologist finds is a radio collar among a scattering of hair and bones, making it difficult to definitively determine the cause of the animal's death.

Insights into reproduction are obtained by determining the pregnancy status of captured females either from levels of hormones in blood samples or detecting a fetus with a portable ultrasound machine. Both survival and reproduction can vary depending on the age of the animal which can be determined based on the irruption pattern of incisor teeth as one pair of deciduous teeth are replaced with permanent incisors annually for the first 3½ years of an animal's life. Older ages can be determined for dead animals by extracting an incisor from the jaw and sending it to a laboratory that can prepare and stain the tooth and count the annual rings of cementum in the root like counting the annual rings of a tree. In addition to these field activities, an equally important aspect of monitoring and conserving mountain ungulate populations in the region is integrating all the various types of data collected in the field. This requires many hours working in the office on computers and often personnel with specialized expertise in sophisticated statistical, mapping, and modeling tools to understand the complex dynamics of populations and inform management decisions.

*Monitoring efforts can include aerial surveys, ground observations, documentation of mortality through radio collars, and health sampling. Photos by Mark Gocke, Wyoming Game and Fish Department (upper left, lower left), Chris Queen, Wyoming Game and Fish Department (upper right), and Bob Garrott, Montana State University (lower right).*

*Mountain goats on Sepulcher Mountain in Yellowstone National Park. Photo by Diane Renkin, National Park Service.*

# Chapter 8
# Impacts of Expanding Introduced Mountain Goats

*Jesse D. DeVoe, Sarah R. Dewey, Douglas E. McWhirter, and Blake Lowrey*

## RANGE EXPANSION

In three quarters of a century, the approximate span of one human lifetime, the number of mountain goats living in the Greater Yellowstone Area increased from no known individuals to about 2,355 in 2014. Mountain goats first appeared in the area through the relocation of 157 individuals to various mountain ranges in efforts by state agencies to increase hunting opportunities for large game (see chapter 2). These relocations began in the 1940s and continued to the early 1970s. From release sites on the periphery of the area, mountain goats began colonizing and expanding their range into the core. While the speed of the expansion has been modest since the initial introductions, the increase in their distribution and abundance has been steady and is ongoing. For example, aerial counts of mountain goats within or near the boundary of Yellowstone National Park increased from 24 in 1997 to 178 in 2009 and 209 in 2014. The current distribution of mountain goats encompasses all the mountain ranges of the northern portion of the Greater Yellowstone Area, as well as the Snake River and, most recently, the Teton Range in the southern portion of the area.

Mountain goats in the area have repeatedly demonstrated an aptitude to disperse across unsuitable habitats, such as low elevations and forested areas, to access and colonize new areas. There are extensive unoccupied, but suitable, mountain ranges such as the southern Absaroka and Wind River ranges in Wyoming. As a result, there is strong likelihood that mountain goat distributions will continue to expand unless managers employ specific actions to curtail their population growth and dispersal. Because of the strong potential for mountain goats to continue expanding their range, and their designation as a non-native species in the area, some natural resource agencies have raised concerns that they may be detrimental to native bighorn sheep. Mountain goats could compete for forage and space, transfer disease-causing pathogens, and negatively affect native plants in subalpine and alpine plant communities. (Laundré 1990, Varley 1996, Lemke 2004, DeVoe et al. 2015, Flesch et al. 2016, Lowrey et al. 2017, National Park Service 2018b)

## RANGE OVERLAP WITH NATIVE BIGHORN SHEEP

Mountain goats and bighorn sheep use similar habitats and share native ranges outside of the Greater Yellowstone Area, primarily in inland mountains west of the continental divide from the northern United States to central Alberta and British Columbia, Canada. The ability of both mountain ungulates to share these ranges and maintain healthy populations is likely due to differences in their selection of seasonal home ranges and habitat types and foods within home ranges. The historic absence of mountain goats in the Greater Yellowstone Area since the Pleistocene may have enabled native bighorn sheep to broaden their range more than would be possible in the presence of mountain goats. Under this scenario, stronger levels of overlap in resource selection and competition would occur where colonizing mountain goats infringe on habitats occupied by bighorn sheep. Within the Greater Yellowstone Area, the welfare of bighorn sheep is of concern to wildlife managers due to substantial historical population declines across most of their range, a consequence of market hunting, habitat loss, and diseases introduced by domestic livestock (see chapter 2). Mountain goats also have the same lethal respiratory diseases that affect bighorn sheep and can transfer these pathogens to them, as has been documented in regions outside of the Greater Yellowstone Area (see chapter 6). The area hosts many isolated populations of bighorn sheep, some of which continue to experience periodic die-offs and poor recruitment from disease, as well as one of the most robust core ranges of bighorn sheep in North America that is largely absent of mountain goats. For these reasons, the continued increase in distribution and abundance of mountain goats poses potential for substantial negative impacts to bighorn sheep populations in the Greater Yellowstone Area. (Adams et al. 1982, Gross 2001, Courtemanch 2014, Wolff et al. 2016, Lowrey et al. 2018a)

Competition for limited resources, such as food, water, minerals, or winter range, can drive one species to dominate over another through aggressive displacement behavior or the exploitation (use) of shared limited resources. In the Front Range of Colorado, researchers observed over 100 interactions between non-native mountain goats and native bighorn sheep and concluded that 37% resulted in the apparent deterrence of bighorn sheep from a resource, such as mineral or foraging sites. However, most interactions were benign with no or only a modest response of bighorn sheep to the presence of mountain goats. Within the Greater Yellowstone Area, we have observed both species bedded, apparently amiably, within 10 yards (9 meters) of each other! We also have photos from remote cameras showing both species appearing to wait their turn to access a salt bait.

While both species broadly overlap in the area, it is unclear how often direct interactions occur. Studies evaluating the direct exploitation of shared limited resources and the effects on both mountain ungulates do not exist. However, comparisons of seasonal diets and habitat attributes have provided insight into the potential overlap in resource use. Separate studies of mountain goat and bighorn sheep diets have found strong overlap in use of forage resources, with both species relying on similar

*A bighorn sheep ram appearing to wait for a pair of mountain goats to finish their turn at a bucket of salt (hidden behind the rock pile) in the Gallatin Range of Montana. Exploitation of limited resources by mountain goats may have negative impacts to bighorn sheep. However, it is unclear how often direct interactions cause displacement and whether these interactions have an impact on bighorn sheep populations. Photo by Bob Garrott, Montana State University.*

proportions and species of grasses and forbs during the summer and winter. However, in shared ranges within the Greater Yellowstone Area, summer diet overlap was substantially lower, with a greater reliance on forbs by mountain goats and grasses by bighorn sheep. While studies in the northeast portion of Yellowstone National Park found greater overlap in fall diets, the two mountain ungulates used distinctive feeding sites, only overlapping use in these feeding sites by 30%. Scientists need more information about dietary overlap between the two mountain ungulates to draw reliable conclusions. (Laundré 1994, Varley 1996, Reed 2001)

While seasonal ranges of introduced mountain goats and native bighorn sheep overlap considerably in portions of the Greater Yellowstone Area (see chapters 3 and 4), comparisons of habitat and home range attributes can provide insights into potential competition. A recent study based on global positioning system (GPS) collar locations in the northeastern portion of the Greater Yellowstone Area, where mountain goats and bighorn sheep have shared home ranges in the same areas for approximately 50 years, found strong similarities in selection for habitat attributes during both summer and winter and, therefore, limited evidence of seasonal partitioning or separation. The strongest differences included slope, with steeper slopes selected more strongly by bighorn sheep during the summer and by mountain goats during the winter. Bighorn sheep avoided canopy cover more strongly during both seasons and tended to occur at lower elevations during winter. However, these differences did not result in complete spatial separation between the two species. (Lowrey et al. 2018b)

Although there appear to be some differences in diet that may reduce the frequency and magnitude of competitive interactions, the seasonal habitats and home ranges of mountain goats and bighorn sheep in the Greater Yellowstone Area are similar enough that the spatial overlap between the two species will likely continue to increase as ranges and numbers of mountain goats expand. Differences in the timing of resource use by each species, as well as the relative abundance of forage and contiguous habitat available across much of the mountain environments in the Greater Yellowstone Area, may lessen competitive interactions and associated effects. We note that numbers of both species increased during the period of mountain goat expansion. However, expanding mountain goats may negatively affect bighorn sheep on shared winter ranges or other areas where these resources are less available or contiguous, particularly if increases in interactions between the two species result in the transmission of respiratory diseases to bighorn sheep. Additionally, given that populations of bighorn sheep and mountain goats in separate geographic areas have strong dietary overlap, it remains uncertain whether mountain goats will adversely affect bighorn sheep once they completely colonize the area and the process of partitioning occurs. (Laundré 1994, Varley 1996, Reed 2001, Flesch et al. 2016, Butler et al. 2017, Lowrey et al. 2018b)

## POTENTIAL IMPACTS TO NATIVE PLANT COMMUNITIES

Native plant communities may be sensitive to activities such as bedding, grazing, trailing, and wallowing (dust baths) by non-native mountain goats. In Olympic National Park, high numbers of mountain goats on summer ranges caused substantial declines in subalpine and alpine plant cover and diversity with detrimental impacts to several rare plant species. Moreover, mountain goats increased bare soil and the abundance of plants that proliferate in disturbed areas. The deposition of nitrogen into the soil from urine and feces of mountain goats may alter rates of nitrogen cycling in subalpine and alpine communities. However, scientists have not detected substantial impacts of mountain goats on plant communities in the Greater Yellowstone Area, even in regions where mountain goats have been present for approximately half a century.

In alpine regions of the northeastern portion of Yellowstone National Park, an area with such a history of mountain goat presence, a study found minimal impacts of mountain goats on native plant species. Biologists documented decreased plant cover, increased bare soil, and increased soil nitrogen in areas of high mountain goat use, but these effects were restricted to the tops of ridgelines. The lack of substantial impact may be due to the relative abundance of forage and habitat for mountain goats in the region. The effects of mountain goats may be more substantial in areas where resources are limited, such as on winter ranges or in areas with low forage availability. Additionally, the resiliency of native plant communities in the Greater Yellowstone Area to mountain goat presence may be due to adaptations to grazing from a suite of native animals such as chipmunks *Neotamias minimus*, yellow-bellied marmots *Marmota flaviventris*, elk, and bighorn sheep, a species never present in the subalpine and alpine communities of Olympic National Park. Given the relatively rapid increases of mountain goats observed in recent years, for example in Grand Teton National Park, additional monitoring and research will help to understand their effects on local and regional alpine and sub-alpine communities. (Houston et al. 1994, Aho 2012)

## POTENTIAL FOR CONTINUED RANGE EXPANSION

Mountain goats likely will continue to expand their distribution into unoccupied mountainous regions of the Greater Yellowstone Area. A recent study found that nearly all areas annually surveyed had increasing numbers of mountain goats and high kid to adult ratios, a factor characteristic of robust, healthy populations. The strongest rates of population growth occurred in areas mountain goats had most recently colonized. This pattern of high growth rates at the front of the range expansion is characteristic of trends observed in other populations of introduced ungulates. When first introduced, the relatively few individuals and abundant resources can lead to large population increases. When numbers of animals increase to the point that available resources in an area cannot support them, some individuals may move to new areas where resources are not limiting, and competition is low. Population growth rates in these new, unoccupied areas are often unbounded for a time until numbers increase to the capacity of the area to support them.

In the Greater Yellowstone Area, the slowly expanding front of the mountain goat range has now encompassed 43% of previously unoccupied areas of suitable habitat, leaving a substantial (2,367 square miles; 6,131 square kilometers) portion of suitable habitat currently unoccupied. Predictions indicate the entire area could support about 5,330 to 8,850 mountain goats if they eventually occupy all suitable habitat (4,149 square miles; 10,745 square kilometers). This level of abundance is about 2½ to 4 times the 2014 estimate of 2,355 mountain goats in the area. However, the eventual abundance of mountain goats in the Greater Yellowstone Area may be constrained by the availability of winter range and competition with other ungulates. While some of the unoccupied areas of suitable habitat are disjunct from each other, dispersing individuals likely do not require contiguous mountain habitats to colonize new areas. The Gallatin Range in the northwestern portion of the Greater Yellowstone Area supports a robust mountain goat population that likely established from animals dispersing from the neighboring Madison Range to the west or the Bridger Range to the north. These movements would have required travel across densely forested or low-elevation valleys. Observations of dispersal movements over a low-elevation prairie landscape in central Montana further suggest that the lack of contiguous suitable habitat will not prevent continued range expansion in the area. (Williams 1999, DeVoe et al. 2015, Flesch et al. 2016)

Mountain goats have already colonized most suitable habitat in Yellowstone National Park, the Snake River Range of Idaho and Wyoming, and the northern portion of the Greater Yellowstone Area, including the northern Absaroka Mountains (see figures 3 and 4 in chapter 2). The remainder of suitable habitat that is currently unoccupied or in the process of becoming colonized includes the southern Absaroka Range south of the North Fork of the Shoshone River (26% of the total suitable habitat in the Greater Yellowstone Area), Wyoming Range (15%), Wind River Range (10%), Teton Range (5%) in Grand Teton National Park, and Gros Ventre Range (3%). The potential for competition with bighorn sheep and the

*A large group of non-native mountain goats on the Beartooth Plateau in Wyoming. Mountain goat populations are robust in portions of the Greater Yellowstone Area and there is a strong likelihood of continued range expansion throughout the unoccupied regions. Photo by Steve Ard, Tracker Aviation, Inc.*

transmission of respiratory pathogens between bighorn sheep and mountain goats in these unoccupied areas is a concern to managers. Native herds of bighorn sheep occupy a substantial portion of these areas and 75% of the currently occupied bighorn sheep range occurs within areas defined as suitable summer habitat for mountain goats. Both the southern Absaroka (south of North Fork Shoshone River) and Wind River Ranges support the Greater Yellowstone Area's largest core regions for bighorn sheep while the Teton Range supports one of the area's smallest and most isolated native populations of bighorn sheep. The southern Absaroka Range, comprising the largest amount of suitable habitat for mountain goats, is at the beginning stages of colonization with only single and small groups of mountain goats recorded. In the adjoining Absaroka Mountains to the north, mountain goats are well established and likely the primary source of dispersing individuals to this region. (DeVoe et al. 2015, Flesch et al. 2016, Lowrey et al. 2018b)

The Teton Range is also experiencing colonization of mountain goats, with the first individuals observed in the late 1970s. These individuals were dispersers from the established population introduced in the Snake River Range of Idaho in the late 1960s and early 1970s. From the late 1970s through the early 2000s, sightings of mountain goats in the Teton Range were sporadic and thought to represent transient individuals. However, from 2008 onwards, biologists at Grand Teton National Park consistently documented adult females with dependent young, signaling that breeding was occurring within the park. Since then, the population has grown steadily and, during the most recent aerial survey in December 2018, biologists counted 88 mountain goats. Presently, most mountain goat activity occurs between Cascade and Snowshoe canyons on the east side of the Tetons within Grand Teton National Park, although biologists have observed mountain goats at the north and south ends of the range as well as the western portion on the Caribou-Targhee National Forest. Based on monitoring of radio-collared mountain goats within Grand Teton National Park, productivity and survival of adult females have been high and all evidence suggests the population was rapidly growing. The predicted amount of suitable habitat available within the Teton Range can support about 250 to 400 mountain goats, a number that is 2.5 to 4 times higher than current population estimates. If left unmanaged, the mountain goat population could colonize all suitable habitats throughout the Teton Range. (Whitfield 1983, Hayden 1984, Laundré 1990, DeVoe et al. 2015, Wyoming Game and Fish Department 2018)

## COMPLEXITIES OF MANAGING MOUNTAIN GOATS

The management of mountain goats in the Greater Yellowstone Area is complex and challenging. Mountain goat populations overlap multiple federal and state jurisdictions, each with differing missions and mandates. Thus, their management requires close coordination between these agencies (see chapter 9). Sixty-seven percent of lands are managed by the federal government, including 48% by the Forest Service (including 11 wilderness areas), 11% by the National Park Service, 7% by the Bureau of Land Management, 0.5% by the Fish & Wildlife Service, 0.1% by the Bureau of Reclamation, and 0.2% by other federal land managers. Private entities own 27% of lands in the Greater Yellowstone Area, with state agencies (4.2%), Native American tribes (1.8%), and non-governmental agencies (0.03%) managing the rest. The primary agencies involved in the management of mountain goats and their habitat include the National Park Service (Yellowstone and Grand Teton national parks), state wildlife management agencies (Idaho Department of Fish and Game; Montana Fish, Wildlife and Parks; Wyoming Game and Fish Department), and the Forest Service (Beaverhead-Deer Lodge, Bridger-Teton, Caribou-Targhee, Custer Gallatin, and Shoshone national forests). (McIntyre and Ellis 2011)

Each agency approaches its responsibility from the standpoint of its own management policies and with different objectives. National Park Service management policies call for the management of exotic, non-native species that do not meet a park purpose. This management could include eradication if control is prudent and feasible and the exotic species interferes with natural processes and the perpetuation of natural features, native species, or natural habitats. The National Park Service has begun removing introduced mountain goats from Olympic National Park in Washington and Grand Teton National Park in Wyoming. Yellowstone National Park has conducted research to determine potential impacts on native plant and animal resources but is not considering a capture and removal program at this time due to the large number of mountain goats involved and significant social, funding, and logistical obstacles. (Houston et al. 1994, National Park Service 2006, Aho 2012, White et al. 2013, National Park Service 2018a,b)

Generally, state management objectives are to sustain populations in suitable habitats while providing a conservative harvest. The Wyoming Game and Fish Department is interested in maintaining mountain goat populations in areas with minimal impact to native bighorn sheep. However, they would like to discourage further expansion by mountain goats into native bighorn sheep populations. The establishment of hunting districts for mountain goats may slow their spread through the rest of the Greater Yellowstone Area, but consistent hunting pressure will be needed to reduce mountain goat abundance. The Forest Service classifies bighorn sheep as a sensitive species on all the National Forest System lands in the area. This designation requires supervisors to maintain viable populations in identified planning units and generally gives them priority for conservation over non-native species such as mountain goats. (U.S. Department of Agriculture, Forest Service 2005)

The interests of hunters and wildlife viewers play an important role in the management of mountain goats by state agencies and the Forest Service, whereas the conservation of native species and communities is a priority for the National Park Service. The challenge in managing introduced mountain goats in a complex administrative landscape like the Greater Yellowstone Area, where a single mountain goat population may occur within several jurisdictions, stems from striving to integrate competing management perspectives and public demands with consideration of the local context. For example, in Wyoming, wildlife managers employ different options for two populations of mountain goats that overlap with bighorn sheep. Bighorn sheep that reside in the Absaroka Mountains share the same respiratory pathogens as mountain goats in that area so disease is less of a concern. In contrast, disease testing suggests lethal pathogens typically associated with pneumonia are not present in bighorn sheep in the Teton Range, even though the likely source population of mountain goats was exposed. In addition, Wyoming Game and Fish Department managers can achieve management goals for mountain goat abundance and distribution through managed hunting in the Absaroka Mountains outside of Yellowstone National Park, while that approach is less effective in the Teton Range because the majority of mountain goats reside within Grand Teton National Park. Therefore, this situation necessitates a very active role of the National Park Service to address mountain goat numbers in the Teton Range, which they have undertaken. Compared to Yellowstone National Park, the number of mountain goats in Grand Teton National Park is also relatively low and, therefore, preventing further expansion of goats would involve the removal of fewer animals, which may be more socially acceptable and reasonable to fund. (Flesch et al. 2016)

As introduced mountain goats continue to expand in the Greater Yellowstone Area, the agencies entrusted with managing them will face additional challenges and difficult decisions, in part because of the complex administrative landscape. With flexibility in management and consideration of region-specific ecological situations, mountain goats can have a place in the area but will be highly managed to preserve native species and communities.

## FUTURE MANAGEMENT OF MOUNTAIN GOATS

Managers intentionally introduced mountain goats into previously unoccupied habitats of the Greater Yellowstone Area to provide hunting and viewing opportunities.

This management approach is not favored today, and there are reasons to actively manage or discourage their expansion. However, it is important to recognize that conservation and perpetuation of mountain goats in areas with minimal conflicts with native species may be desirable for some management agencies. For example, areas like the Snake River Range in Idaho and Wyoming have a long history of mountain goat presence with little to no overlap with native herds of bighorn sheep. The Idaho Department of Fish and Game and the Wyoming Game and Fish Department manage for the perpetuation of robust mountain goat populations in these areas for public hunting and viewing opportunities.

However, in areas where impacts of mountain goats on native species may be substantial, management of mountain goats is, and will likely continue to be, more direct and active. This is particularly true in regions where managers are concerned about the welfare of important bighorn sheep populations. Many of the strategies for managing mountain goats across the Greater Yellowstone Area attempt to reduce the opportunities for mountain goats to use or become established in areas occupied by native bighorn sheep. For example, the population of bighorn sheep in the Teton Range is especially sensitive due to its constricted range, small size, unique genetic and behavioral adaptations, and susceptibility to pneumonia-causing pathogens. Although mountain goats have been in the Teton Range for nearly four decades, recent evidence of breeding has prompted Grand Teton National Park, in coordination with the Wyoming Game and Fish Department and the Forest Service, to initiate plans for reducing or eliminating the potential for mountain goats to overlap with bighorn sheep. (Wyoming State-wide Bighorn-Domestic Sheep Interaction Working Group 2004, Butler et al. 2017, National Park Service 2018b)

The Absaroka Range provides another example of the strong emphasis on bighorn sheep conservation in management plans for mountain goats. The entire range supports one of the largest and most robust populations of bighorn sheep in the continental United States, with an estimated 4,000 animals spread in herds across the landscape. These core native herds were never extirpated or supplemented to increase their numbers and are home to over 85% of the bighorn sheep that reside in Wyoming. The southern portion of the Absaroka Range supports approximately the same abundance of bighorn sheep as predicted for mountain goats, an estimated 1,395 to 2,315 animals. The Wyoming Game and Fish Department places the highest priority on the native herds of bighorn sheep across the entire Absaroka Range. Management of these native herds attempts to maintain the unique genetic and behavioral adaptations that bighorn sheep possess in these areas. Therefore, the Wyoming Game and Fish Department has implemented liberal mountain goat hunting seasons in the Absaroka Range outside of Yellowstone National Park. The Colorado Division of Wildlife and Parks uses a similar management approach to discourage mountain goats from colonizing important bighorn sheep habitat. (Wyoming Statewide Bighorn Sheep-Domestic Sheep Interaction Working Group 2004, Colorado Division of Wildlife 2009, Wolff et al. 2016, Lowrey et al. 2018b)

Although managers have achieved many successes, setbacks and failures have stymied restoration efforts for several bighorn sheep populations. This is clearly illustrated by the fact that range-wide translocation of over 21,500 bighorn sheep associated with restoration efforts has ultimately resulted in a current population of only 50,000 animals. As a result, there is more emphasis on maintaining existing populations, especially large groups of populations such as those in the Greater Yellowstone Area. Many of these populations have a portfolio of diverse migratory patterns that may be difficult to recreate using translocation. This effort will require assessing and making management decisions related to acceptable risk regarding pathogen transfer, competition with mountain goats and domestic livestock, increasing human developments and activities within bighorn sheep habitats, and potential habitat and environmental modifications that climate change may exacerbate. (Wild Sheep Working Group 2012, Lowrey et al. 2019)

Furthermore, a substantial proportion of bighorn sheep in the Greater Yellowstone Area occupy high-elevation winter ranges as an integral component of their seasonal habitats. Bighorn sheep that rely on these winter ranges are dependent upon a very delicate interplay of dry, windblown, snow-free ridges that exist through mid- to late winter followed by movements to gradually opening areas as snow melts at lower elevations. Increasing temperatures at these high elevations during winter could disrupt this balance by creating freeze-thaw cycles that render forage unavailable and/or produce a mismatch in the timing of movements to lower-elevation areas in spring. Such developments could result in habitats being able to support fewer bighorn sheep and have population-level impacts. Such impacts may worsen in the presence of competitors, such as mountain goats. (Courtemanch et al. 2017)

Disease-related mortality is an all too common component of bighorn sheep populations. Efforts to understand the disease ecology of bighorn sheep are essential for maintaining or recovering bighorn sheep populations. Increased knowledge of pathogen transmission between bighorn sheep, mountain goats, and domestic livestock, as well as transmission within bighorn sheep populations and pathogen persistence once introduced into populations, is necessary for identifying options to manage disease and minimize mortality. In addition to disease, continued research and monitoring of bighorn sheep and mountain goat populations through time as their distribution, population dynamics, and habitats change is necessary to make informed management decisions in the future. In addition, in the Greater Yellowstone Area, continued coordination and collaboration on research and management among various federal, state, and tribal agencies is indispensable to accomplish these goals.

## CONCLUSIONS

Managers intentionally introduced mountain goats into the Greater Yellowstone Area during the 1950s to1970s to provide hunting and viewing opportunities.

Since these introductions, mountain goat populations have grown to over 2,000 individuals in approximately 43% of the suitable habitat. However, there may be several reasons to intentionally manage or discourage their expansion. Although biologists have not detected significant impacts to native flora in the area from mountain goats, there is potential for them to affect native bighorn sheep populations through competition and transmission of disease-causing pathogens. It is highly probable that mountain goats will continue to expand throughout the area and infringe on habitats occupied by bighorn sheep. The Greater Yellowstone Area could potentially support up to nearly 9,000 mountain goats if they colonize all available habitat, the large majority of which is in habitats occupied by bighorn sheep. Even if there are low levels of shared resource use between mountain goats and bighorn sheep, it seems doubtful that this many mountain goats would not have adverse impacts on the almost 6,000 bighorn sheep that currently reside in the area.

Nonetheless, it is important to recognize and appreciate how mountain goats are perfectly suited for the mountainous habitats of the Greater Yellowstone Area and that mountain goats are highly regarded in many regions of the area by wildlife watchers and hunters. Given the complex ecological, jurisdictional, and social landscape in the area, there is not one single solution for managing mountain goats throughout the area. In areas where mountain goats minimally conflict with native species, namely bighorn sheep, there may be reason to promote their conservation. As mountain goats continue to expand in the Greater Yellowstone Area, the need for continued cross-jurisdictional coordination and collaboration in both research and management will be necessary to accomplish objectives of the myriad agencies that align with social desires in the area. Continued monitoring of populations through time and research focused on disease ecology for the two mountain ungulates are necessities to inform management decisions in the future. (DeVoe et al. 2015, Lowrey et al. 2018b)

## HOW WE LEARN: IMPACTS OF MOUNTAIN GOATS

Owing to the inclination of mountain goats and bighorn sheep to inhabit some of the most rugged and remote terrain of the Greater Yellowstone Area, designing and conducting rigorous studies to understand the ecology of these mountain ungulates is a challenging endeavor. Not only do such studies often require long, large elevation-gain approaches on foot or expensive aerial flights to access their habitat, but just observing the highly mobile animals amidst ledges and cliffs or underneath forest canopies poses an additional impediment to obtaining good information on mountain ungulates. To overcome these challenges and gain insight into the potential exploitative competition from overlap of home ranges and resource use by mountain goats and bighorn sheep, researchers in the Greater Yellowstone Area have employed several innovative techniques for collecting information on movement patterns, distributions, and resource selection. One method is the use of VHF and GPS collars placed on captured animals, which have provided a wealth of ecological information (see chapters 3 and 4). The use of this technology is highly desirable; however, they are costly to deploy across large areas of the Greater Yellowstone Area landscape. A more cost-efficient and entirely non-invasive method of collecting information on mountain ungulates includes the use of camera traps. The ability to collect broad spatial data is limited by this method, however, due to the restricted locations camera traps need to be placed to be most effective.

Another alternative is the use of occupancy methods, whereby biologists address the limitations of animal detections by recording both the presence and absence of animals in an area. For example, aerial surveys often record only the location of animals where the observers looked. However, if observers do not record the sites where they looked and did not see animals, they do not know if the animal was absent

*A camera placed at a high-elevation site in the northern Beartooth Range captures a group of bighorn rams followed by a group of mountain goats less than 24 hours later, demonstrating how camera traps can be used to capture overlap of resource use between the two mountain ungulate species. Photos by Doug McWhirter, Wyoming Game and Fish Department.*

*Example of occupancy survey methods for understanding fine-scale habitat selection of mountain ungulates from a study completed in the Greater Yellowstone Area (DeVoe et al. 2015). Two independent observers were placed at each viewshed survey point and simultaneously recorded both detections and non-detections of mountain ungulates in a survey viewshed of 100 meter by 100 meter grid cells. These methods allow estimation of fine-scale habitat selection corrected for poor detection of mountain ungulates on complex and difficult to survey landscapes. Photos by Jesse DeVoe, Montana State University.*

or went undetected. Occupancy studies take advantage of the additional 'absence' information, as well as data collected from a second, independent observer, to make improved inferences of species habitat selection and distributions. Biologists used this method recently in the Greater Yellowstone Area to understand summer habitat selection and predict the potential expansion and abundance of mountain goats in uncolonized areas. Equipped with binoculars, spotting scopes, and ruggedized field tablets, researchers backpacked into mountain ungulate terrain and visited numerous survey points from which two independent observers surveyed view sheds of 100 meters by 100 meters (109 yards by 109 yards) grid cells (visible on the field tablets). To estimate habitat selection by mountain goats, biologists recorded the presence or absence of mountain goat groups in each grid cell and related this information to remotely sensed habitat attributes. They modeled these habitat selection relationships across the entire Greater Yellowstone Area and combined the results with estimates of abundance from areas in the Greater Yellowstone Area fully colonized by mountain goats to estimate the total number of mountain goats the entire area could support. While highly informative, these methods are time and energy consuming, not only due to accessing rugged and remote terrain (multi-day trips are essential), but also collecting both presence and absence information requires greater effort than presence-only information. (DeVoe et al. 2015)

*A bighorn sheep ram atop a seemingly insurmountable rock pillar. Photo by Randy Ilg.*

# Chapter 9
# Current Management

*Douglas E. McWhirter, Julie A. Cunningham,*
*Hollie M. Miyasaki, P. J. White, and Sarah R. Dewey*

## JURISDICTIONS AND MANDATES

The North American Model of Wildlife Management is premised on the public ownership of wildlife, which is not the case in most of the world where wildlife is owned by private landowners or governments. With some exceptions, the primary legal authority and management responsibility for sustaining wildlife populations is entrusted to state agencies governed by commissions which, in the Greater Yellowstone Area, include the Idaho Department of Fish and Game, Montana Department of Fish, Wildlife and Parks, and the Wyoming Game and Fish Department. Federal land management agencies such as the Forest Service and the Bureau of Land Management are responsible for managing wildlife habitat and fulfilling other multiple use objectives within their jurisdictions. Also, the Fish and Wildlife Service works with state, federal, and tribal agencies and private landowners to recover federally designated threatened and endangered species, coordinates management of migratory birds that seasonally cross jurisdictional boundaries and manages habitats through their wildlife refuge system. In addition, the National Park Service has responsibility for the management of wildlife and habitat within Yellowstone and Grand Teton national parks. This arrangement of jurisdictions with variable responsibilities with respect to wildlife and their habitats necessitates a collaborative approach to management. (Organ et al. 2012)

With respect to state wildlife agencies, management usually entails the establishment of specific objectives and management activities that direct populations toward those objectives. In the case of large ungulates, this includes managing population sizes through hunting, habitat enhancement, landowner agreements, and other actions. Many states have species-specific management plans that detail these objectives and management actions. (Idaho Department of Fish and Game 2010, Montana Fish, Wildlife and Parks 2010)

A somewhat different approach is employed on National Park Service lands, where populations can fluctuate more in response to competition, forage availability, predation, and weather, with less human intervention. As an example, hunting in Yellowstone National Park was prohibited by Congress in 1894 (16 USC 26). While desirable non-native species may be included in the management objectives of state agencies, National Park Service policy recommends the management of non-native species that interfere with native wildlife or their habitats, up to and including eradication, if such control is prudent and feasible. (National Park Service 2006)

Although management mandates vary among agencies and jurisdictions, there is much overlap of shared goals, including conserving or recovering sustainable populations of wildlife and their habitats while maintaining the public trust by basing decisions on reliable information and reducing property damage and human injury. As a result, migratory populations, like many of the ungulate herds in the Greater Yellowstone Area, require a coordinated approach to management.

## POPULATION MANAGEMENT

Management can be broadly defined as the process of dealing with or controlling things or people. Ungulate management is most often the latter, and may mean increasing, decreasing, or maintaining the size of a wildlife population, which is primarily accomplished through controlling people (in this case, hunters). State wildlife agencies, with public involvement, usually establish some sort of population objective, which is often

*Surveying for bighorn sheep on winter range with a helicopter in Montana. Photo by Mark Gocke, Wyoming Game and Fish Department.*

a combination of biological and social capacities, and which can be used as a measure of success and provide agency accountability. Monitoring populations provides indicators used to assess whether established objectives are being met. This monitoring can include periodic "trend counts," population estimates derived from sampling the population and applying statistical analyses, or other attributes such as ram to ewe ratios or success rates of hunters (see chapter 7).

A concept referred to as adaptive management is often used in population manage= ment due to unpredictable environmental variation, difficulties in collecting data, and the need to make assumptions regarding the drivers of population dynamics in the absence of complete and detailed site-specific information. Adaptive management is a continual process of evaluation and adjustment that includes determining an objective, applying a management action, measuring progress towards achieving the objective, and adjusting subsequent management actions. A prerequisite of population management is understanding the dynamics of a population, or factors responsible for its growth or decline, so appropriate measures can be taken to manage toward objectives. Sometimes monitoring information is enough to gain this understanding, but often more detailed knowledge is required, which can be provided through specific research as part of the adaptive management process. (Walters 1986, Riley et al. 2003)

Hunting is the primary tool used to meet population objectives and, as traditionally applied to both bighorn sheep and mountain goats in the Greater Yellowstone Area, has been quite conservative. Bighorn sheep hunting usually involves limited numbers of hunters and is focused on adult males. In Montana, hunter harvest of bighorn sheep ewes is applied in specific areas to maintain densities below a given threshold, often the forage capacity of that specific winter range, to prevent excessive winter mortalities and minimize the risk of disease outbreaks. The ability to offer ewe licenses exists in Wyoming and Idaho but has not been implemented in a substantial way. In contrast to male-only harvest in bighorn sheep, either-sex hunting of mountain goats (adopted primarily due to difficulty distinguishing males and females) is the norm to control or reduce mountain goat numbers.

Another way of managing populations is to remove the annual increase created by the birth and recruitment of young animals by capturing and translocating individuals. Bighorn sheep and mountain goats have traditionally been captured using drop nets, corral traps, chemical immobilization and, more recently, aerial net-gunning operations. For example, the size of the Whiskey Mountain bighorn sheep herd in Wyoming was controlled for many years through the capture and relocation of 75 to 100 bighorn sheep each year (1,574 total from 1964 to 1990), which had the additional benefit of restoring or supplementing other bighorn sheep populations. Similarly, from 1989 to 1997 a total of 46 mountain goats were removed from the Snake River Range herd in Idaho to prevent the population from growing beyond its' carrying capacity. In some areas, extenuating circumstances such as a lack of hunter access create situations where translocations are employed out of necessity. (Idaho Department of Fish and Game 2019)

## HABITAT MANAGEMENT

While population management is important, no species can persist without habitat. Land management agencies bear responsibility to maintain habitats for native species and, in some cases, desirable non-native species (see chapter 3). This usually means managing land uses such as oil and gas development, road building, timber harvesting, livestock grazing, and recreation to minimize impacts on wildlife resources as much as possible. In the case of livestock grazing, the land management agency may also consider the effects of diseases introduced from livestock as an impact on the persistence of certain wildlife species, as in the case of domestic sheep grazing and potential pathogen transmission risk to bighorn sheep (see chapter 6).

In addition to habitat protection, land management agencies also can enhance habitats with prescribed fire, managed wildfire, timber harvest, and herbicide treatments.

*Mountain ungulates are captured through a variety of techniques, from (clockwise from upper left) net-gunning from a helicopter, drop nets, darting with immobilization drugs, and self-triggered net/mesh traps. Photos by Mark Gocke, Wyoming Game and Fish Department (upper left, lower right), Richard Horst (upper right), and Doug McWhirter, Wyoming Game and Fish Department (lower left).*

*Bighorn sheep feeding in habitat recently burned by wildfire. Burned areas offer highly nutritious forage and high visibility and are sought out by bighorn sheep. Photo by Mark Gocke, Wyoming Game & Fish Department.*

Bighorn sheep are grazers that prefer open habitats with high visibility, so fire and mechanical treatments that remove vision-obstructing trees and shrubs and increase the production of preferred forage grasses are beneficial. Depending upon the goal, herbicides can be used to remove shrubs to achieve the same response, or to discourage the establishment of undesirable weeds like cheatgrass that often follow disturbances like wild or prescribed fires. (Risenhoover and Bailey 1985, Festa-Bianchet 1988)

## DISEASE MANAGEMENT

Bighorn sheep and mountain goats are susceptible to pneumonia and, therefore, disease prevention and management is an important undertaking (see chapter 6). Knowing what respiratory pathogens exist in a herd is valuable, and this information is gathered from periodic disease surveillance. Knowledge of existing pathogens is also important from a restoration standpoint because new pathogens can be introduced when translocating animals. (Besser et al. 2012b, Cassirer et al. 2017a)

Bighorn sheep are generally susceptible to common pathogens harbored by domestic sheep and goats, so minimizing the potential for pathogen transmission from domestic sheep and goats to bighorn sheep is an objective for wildlife managers. Considerable efforts are expended to avoid commingling using intensive and collaborative approaches to administering domestic sheep grazing allotments and negotiating waivers (with financial compensation) of specific grazing allotments. Even though primarily benefitting bighorn sheep, such "buy-outs" have also helped individual permittees experiencing depredations from recovered large carnivores such as grizzly bears and wolves. However, the reduction of domestic grazing opportunities from public lands is a very controversial issue, with involuntary actions often litigated. (Schommer and Woolever 2008, Wild Sheep Working Group 2012)

The concern over pathogen transmission is great enough that state wildlife agencies may cull individuals showing signs of diseases such as pneumonia from a bighorn herd in the hope of removing infected animals and minimizing the spread of disease. The lethal removal of bighorn sheep observed commingling with domestic sheep or goats is another tactic used to minimize pathogen transfer and the spread of disease. The concern is these bighorn sheep may become infected, return to their herd of origin, and introduce new pathogens to the remainder of the herd and initiate a disease outbreak. In very specific cases, domestic sheep producers have been given the authority to lethally remove bighorn sheep if they appear among their domestic sheep. If a domestic sheep is wandering or left after others have been brought off grazing allotments, state wildlife agencies may occasionally be given permission from the owner to remove that animal. As one might imagine, lethally removing someone's private property is a task handled very delicately. In some cases, ownership cannot easily be established, and responses are limited. Idaho Code Title 25, Chapter 23 and Montana MCA 81-4-6 and MCA 81-4-2 address disposition of stray livestock and Wyoming has adopted a feral, or "stray" livestock statute (§11-48-102) that establishes a protocol for removing such animals if they pose disease risks.

To find collaborative solutions to address overlap or commingling between domestic and wild sheep and the resulting pathogen transmission concerns, a diverse group of stakeholders in Wyoming developed a Statewide Bighorn Sheep-Domestic Sheep Interaction Plan. This plan prioritizes the state's bighorn sheep herds with respect to their origin and importance, with core native herds receiving the highest level of protection, and translocated herds receiving less emphasis. As part of this plan, there is also agreement on how these issues will be addressed and, most importantly, encouragement to continue communication among all interested parties. To define areas of concern for pathogen transmission risk, the Forest Service developed a computer model that quantifies the relative risk of contact between bighorn sheep and domestic sheep grazing allotments on public lands. The resulting information serves as a starting point for discussions on how to reduce that risk.

(Wyoming Statewide Bighorn Sheep-Domestic Sheep Interaction Working Group 2004, O'Brien et al. 2014, U.S. Department of Agriculture, Forest Service, and U.S. Department of Interior, Bureau of Land Management 2015)

Other prevention options such as identification and removal of chronically infected pathogen "carriers" and vaccines could have benefits, although field administration in wild, remote settings where bighorn sheep exist could prove problematic. Vaccines or the administration of antibiotics to domestic sheep may eventually prove more feasible, although increased costs are still likely. Prevention of commingling currently remains the most effective means of minimizing the risk of pathogen transmission.

## FUNDING

Most federal funding for ungulate management comes from congressionally appropriated taxpayer dollars. State agency work is largely funded through hunting license sales and the Federal Aid in Wildlife Restoration Act. Often referred to as the Pittman-Robertson Act, this excise tax on arms and ammunition is used to fund wildlife surveys and research, acquisition and improvement of wildlife habitat, translocations, acquisition and development of public access, and hunter safety programs.

Funding for state management of mountain ungulates is often limited, as agency revenues generated by hunting license sales for these species do not cover the cost of annual population and disease monitoring, let alone intensive research projects or translocation efforts. Programs that generate more hunting revenue, like mule deer or elk, often subsidize the management costs of mountain ungulates, and are generally focused on funding population monitoring efforts. Funding is also generated by the limited special auction or raffle of bighorn sheep and mountain goat hunting licenses. Montana offers one Governor's license for bighorn sheep while Wyoming offers five Governor's licenses for bighorn sheep. Idaho offers two special tags, one available for auction and the other available through a lottery. Although the number of licenses and how the money is funneled into management varies, the money raised can be significant.

The single Montana Governor's bighorn sheep license has sold for as much as $480,000. Montana and Wyoming also offer mountain goat raffles, which generate considerable, but less, funding than bighorn sheep tags ($10,000 to $15,000).

Another source of funding for mountain ungulate management and research efforts are conservation groups such as the Wild Sheep Foundation and their network of chapters and affiliates. Similarly, the Rocky Mountain Goat Alliance dedicates their efforts to mountain goats. In addition, businesses such as Canon USA, Inc. and private donors sometimes provide substantial donations for mountain ungulate research and restoration through foundations and partnership organizations such as Yellowstone Forever and the Grand Teton National Park Foundation. Large, long-term efforts like bighorn sheep and mountain goat research in the Greater Yellowstone Area require support from a broad coalition of funding sources.

## Bighorn Sheep Management

Efforts to re-establish Rocky Mountain bighorn sheep populations (not to be confused with the desert bighorn sheep subspecies) have largely been successful and numbers range-wide have increased from an estimated 10,000 in 1960 to approximately 50,000 in 2017. Most of this increase has been the result of translocations. Between 1920 and 1990, the states of Wyoming, Montana, and Idaho translocated almost 3,000 bighorn sheep within their borders, imported another 300 bighorn sheep, and provided over 600 bighorn sheep to restoration efforts in other states. West-wide, there have been almost 1,500 translocations involving 21,500 bighorn sheep. (Buechner 1960, Wild Sheep Working Group 2015)

These translocations were largely conducted with relatively small numbers of bighorn sheep, and oftentimes with only one release site; usually low-elevation winter ranges due to their accessibility during winter when bighorn sheep are easier to capture. The resulting reestablished herds often reside in relatively homogeneous groups and tend to become sedentary compared to their migratory predecessors. Such restorations leave populations extremely susceptible to disease, weather, and predation influences. Even today, over 50% of bighorn sheep populations in Idaho, Montana, and Wyoming contain less than 100 individuals. (Jesmer et al. 2018)

Recent work has shown the importance of geographically distributed metapopulations (group of connected populations) in the Greater Yellowstone Area. Animals spread throughout suitable habitats and exhibiting a broad range of behavioral traits, such as migration strategies, provide resilience in the face of disease epidemics or severe weather events. Similar examples come from the world of caterpillars and salmon, where such diversity of behaviors has been termed a "portfolio" effect. This term, taken from the world of financial investments, represents the notion that it is best not to have all your eggs in one basket, but instead, to have a diverse portfolio (see chapter 4). (Schindler et al. 2015a, Lowrey et al. 2019)

If a metapopulation is lost, can it be recreated? One management experiment in southwestern Montana is attempting to create a metapopulation using a series of within-mountain range transplants. Along the southwestern face of the Madison Range, there were at least five known, historic bighorn sheep winter ranges. However, bighorn sheep were extant on only two of these five as of 2013. One of these winter ranges had recovered from an all-age, disease-related die-off to record numbers. Biologists created a proposal to move bighorn sheep from this highly-populated winter range to one of the ranges where bighorn sheep had been extinct for at least the past 50 years, with the hope of re-establishing bighorn use of the area. Transplanting bighorn sheep from local source herds has several advantages, including little or no risk of introducing new pathogens (which can occur if another herd is used), familiarity with ecological (habitat) conditions, and retained knowledge of migration behaviors and predator communities. Recent work in the Madison Range indicates there is potential habitat for two to four times the number of bighorn sheep that currently exist, suggesting habitat is not limiting for bighorn sheep and further encouraging this sort of method for re-establishing a metapopulation. (Butler et al. 2018, Lula et al. 2020)

To test this re-establishment plan, biologists moved 97 bighorn sheep over a series of three transplants to a release site approximately 14 airline miles (22 kilometers) north of the capture site. The bighorn sheep were let out of a trailer immediately into their new landscape and showed highly variable individual exploratory behaviors, colonizing the expected winter range and five additional sub-drainages. Most ewes chose low-elevation winter ranges, but some chose high-elevation winter ranges. While some transplanted bighorn travelled nearly 40 miles (64 kilometers) away to join other herds, others remained at the release site a variable number of months, some nearly two years. The released bighorn did show a higher mortality rate than resident bighorn, which was expected as they adjusted to their new landscape. Renewed knowledge of new areas of the Madison Range should now have been thoroughly "injected" into these bighorn sheep, and the extent to which they use them has yet to be determined. Currently, it appears bighorn sheep have remained at the transplant site after each release, gradually rebuilding use through the survival and reproduction of those bighorn sheep from prior years' transplants. (Singer and Gudorf 1999, Cunningham et al. 2018, Lula et al. 2020)

The result of such population conservation and restoration efforts is the increased ability to provide viewing experiences and hunting opportunities for bighorn sheep and mountain goats. Wildlife viewing is a major attraction for visitation to the Greater Yellowstone Area, with tourism contributing substantial economic benefits to communities in the region. For example, more than 4 million people visited Yellowstone National Park during 2019 and spent almost $507 million in communities near the park, which supported about 7,000 jobs and had a cumulative benefit of about $642 million to the area's economy. Similarly, 3.4 million visitors to Grand Teton National Park in 2019 spent almost $630 million in local gateway communities, supporting about 8,640 jobs with a cumulative benefit of $796 million added to the economy. These economic benefits stem, in large part, directly from the preservation of abundant populations of wildlife that often can be viewed and photographed from roads. More than 95% of visitors to the park participated in wild-

*A photographer viewing and photographing bighorn sheep. Bighorn sheep often spend the winter in valley bottoms, and are especially accessible during this time. Photo by Kenneth R. Whitten.*

*A hunter glassing for a bighorn ram in mid-September in the alpine sheep habitats typical of the Greater Yellowstone Area. Photo by Craig Sax, Wyoming Game and Fish Department.*

life viewing during their visits, which exceeded geyser viewing (87%), hiking (39%), camping (27%), and fishing (13%). (Duffield et al. 2000a,b; Manni et al. 2007, Resource Systems Group 2017, Cullinane Thomas and Koontz 2020)

In addition to viewing, over 400 people get the very coveted opportunity to hunt bighorn sheep each year in Idaho, Montana, and Wyoming, which results in approximately 350 rams taken annually, with 158 of these coming from the Greater Yellowstone Area in 2018. The odds of drawing a bighorn sheep license vary from state to state and area to area, but in 2018 almost 50,000 people applied for the 436 available bighorn sheep licenses in Idaho, Montana, and Wyoming (0.9% drawing odds). In a novel way to provide sheep hunting opportunities, certain bighorn sheep hunting districts in Montana have unlimited (one per hunter) licenses available and harvest is managed through a quota system: once the quota is met the district closes upon 48 hours' notice. Quotas in these areas are usually low, generally two to three bighorn sheep rams. Such conservative harvest management contrasts with species such as elk, which exceed 80,000 animals harvested each year among the three states. Although perhaps difficult for some to understand, hunting engenders respect and appreciation for the hunted species and ensures support for their persistence and conservation of their habitats.

## MOUNTAIN GOAT MANAGEMENT

Although there is prehistoric evidence of mountain goats in the Greater Yellowstone Area, they are generally considered a non-native species. Native species evolved in, or migrated to, an area with no human intervention and are particularly adapted to habitats found there. Conversely, non-native species were either intentionally or accidentally introduced to an area by human activities. Although disagreement exists over whether non-native species threaten the natural environment and under what circumstances, there is potential for non-native species to out-compete, transmit pathogens, and adversely affect native species. (Sagaff 2005, Simberloff 2005)

*Capturing and translocating mountain ungulates is difficult but was even more of an epic adventure in the 1940s. These images depict efforts to establish mountain goats in the Greater Yellowstone Area, and involved horse-packing and rafting animals from trap sites to where they could be loaded onto trucks, driven as close to the release site as possible, and then taken by mule-drawn wagons the rest of the way. Photos courtesy of Montana Fish, Wildlife and Parks.*

Mountain goat populations increased through translocations into previously unoccupied habitat in the Greater Yellowstone Area. A total of 17 translocations involving 157 mountain goats occurred (14 releases of 145 mountain goats in Montana and 3 releases of 12 mountain goats in Idaho), and have resulted in a current population of about 2,100 mountain goats, and a broad expansion of their distribution. The translocations of mountain goats in Montana were monumental efforts that included corral traps, pack horses, rafts, and mule-drawn wagons to get animals from their source population in the Sun River area of northwestern Montana to the mountain ranges of the Greater Yellowstone Area (see chapter 2). (Hayden 1984, Cote and Festa-Bianchet 2003, Lemke 2004, McWhirter 2004, Whittlesey et al. 2018, Whittlesey and Bone 2020)

Although responses vary geographically and through time, when compared with bighorn sheep, mountain goat translocations in the Greater Yellowstone Area have been considerably more successful, even with very few founding individuals. As stated earlier, a total of 21,500 bighorn sheep have been translocated that have resulted in a current total range-wide population of 50,000 while 145 mountain goats released into the Greater Yellowstone Area created a current population of 2,100 mountain goats. Another way to look at this is bighorn sheep translocations have produced a 2 to 1 "return on investment" while mountain goats have produced a 15 to 1 return. This may merely reflect the disease sensitivities of bighorn sheep compared to mountain goats, or that bighorn sheep are more of a metapopulation-oriented species, which is difficult to maintain or create in today's landscape.

Even though mountain goats were intentionally introduced into previously unoccupied habitat to provide hunting and viewing opportunities, there may be reasons to intentionally manage or discourage their expansion. Mountain goats and bighorn sheep can harbor the same lethal respiratory pathogens. They also exhibit substantial overlap in their use of habitats and forage species, which can have adverse impacts if both species are trying to share very restricted high-elevation winter ranges.

Research has shown the potential for as many as 5,372 to 8,918 mountain goats in occupied bighorn sheep habitats around the Greater Yellowstone Area. Even if there is some level of shared resources, it is doubtful there could be this many mountain goats and not have adverse impacts on the almost 6,000 bighorn sheep that currently reside in the region. (DeVoe 2015, Wolff et al. 2016, Lowrey et al. 2018a)

Descendants of mountain goats introduced in the Absaroka and Madison mountain ranges of Montana have almost completely colonized suitable habitat within Yellowstone National Park. Mountain goats are breeding and at relatively high abundance (more than 200) in the northeast and northwest portions of the park, with suitable, continuous habitat along the eastern and western boundaries. With more than 600 goats in and adjacent to Yellowstone National Park, mountain goats will likely continue to occupy these habitats and disperse into and out of the park for the foreseeable future. National Park Service (2006) policy allows for the removal of non-native species that interfere with native wildlife or habitats if such control is prudent and feasible. Eradication or control programs to substantially reduce mountain goats would involve intrusive and costly aerial and ground operations in hazardous mountainous terrain for multiple years. Also, many park staff and visitors consider mountain goats valuable, charismatic components of the ecosystem, making the removal or killing of mountain goats in the park a highly sensitive issue. (Schullery and Whittlesey 2001, Lemke 2004, DeVoe 2015, Flesch et al. 2016)

Other national park units are approaching the management of exotic or non-native mountain goats differently in response to specific situations such as the number of animals, geography and proximity to a source population, and threats occurring in each unit. For example, in Rocky Mountain National Park and Dinosaur National Monument, where breeding populations of mountain goats are not established but occasionally appear, protocols developed in cooperation with the states of Colorado and Utah direct the removal of mountain goats as soon as possible after they are detected. In 2018, Olympic National Park began implementing a mountain goat management plan, aimed at removing all mountain goats from the park. The need for removal stems from concerns about mountain goat impacts on sensitive vegetation communities as well as safety concerns following the fatal goring of a park visitor in 2010. Grand Teton National Park has initiated the removal of mountain goats from the park to reduce the potential for disease transmission and competition for space and forage between mountain goats and a small native population of bighorn sheep that is struggling. Park staff want to protect other park resources and values from a growing and expanding mountain goat population. (National Park Service 2016, 2018a,b)

Mountain goats originally translocated into the Snake River Range of Idaho from 1969 through 1971 were first seen in Wyoming on a tributary of the Snake River Canyon in 1975, followed by an observation on Teton Pass in 1977, and another in Grand Teton National Park in 1979. Observations within Grand Teton National Park were relatively sporadic until nannies with kids were first observed in 2008, representing the establishment of a breeding population. The population has dramatically increased since then, with numbers of mountain goats seen during annual aerial surveys surpassing that of bighorn sheep by 2018, with each estimated to consist of approximately 100 individuals. Bighorn sheep in the Tetons are a core native herd that has never been extirpated or supplemented and, with other core native herds in the Absaroka Mountains, northern Wind River Mountains, and the Gros Ventre and Hoback River drainages, are the highest priority bighorn sheep herds in the state to the Wyoming Game and Fish Department.

Although once containing a migratory population segment, bighorn sheep in the Tetons are now restricted to subsisting year-round on high-elevation ranges above 8,500 feet (2,590 meters). Although past concerns regarding pathogen transfer from domestic sheep have been resolved through the retirement and relocation of domestic sheep grazing, current impacts include conifer encroachment into preferred habitats as a result of fire suppression and disturbance from backcountry recreation.

The expansion of mountain goats into bighorn sheep habitats, especially restricted high-elevation winter ranges, creates concern over competition for forage and space as well as risk of pathogen transfer from mountain goats to bighorn sheep. As a result, and even though it may be difficult and costly to implement, Grand Teton National Park has initiated efforts to remove mountain goats from the Tetons, using a combination of both lethal and non-lethal techniques. (Whitfield 1983, Whitfield and Keller 1984, McWhirter 2004, Wyoming Statewide Bighorn Sheep-Domestic Sheep Interaction Working Group 2004, Courtemanch 2014, National Park Service 2018b)

At least in Wyoming, work has shown that bighorn sheep in the Absaroka Mountains already share all lethal pathogens of concern with mountain goats, and so disease risk is perhaps less than that in the Tetons where bighorn sheep have not been exposed to these pathogens. Also, the proportion of bighorn sheep habitat potentially affected by mountain goats in Yellowstone National Park is relatively minor compared with that outside the park. This coupled with the fact that the abundance and distribution of mountain goats outside of Yellowstone can be controlled through hunting seasons means the Wyoming Game and Fish Department can achieve management goals more completely through managed hunting in the Absaroka Mountains than in the Tetons. (Lowrey et al. 2018b)

Therefore, the Wyoming Game and Fish Department has determined where to manage for abundant mountain goats and where to manage for low densities or prevent their expansion altogether. Long-occupied habitats in the Beartooth and Snake River ranges will continue to be managed for robust mountain goat populations, while very liberal hunting seasons for mountain goats have been implemented in the Teton and Absaroka mountains. The Colorado Division of Wildlife and Parks has a similar management approach where mountain goat colonization of high-priority bighorn sheep habitats is actively discouraged. Idaho and Montana both have native populations of mountain goats, some sympatric with bighorn sheep, but do not prioritize one over the other. (Colorado Division of Wildlife 2009)

Even though mountain goats are considered non-native, and significant concerns exist regarding their potential impacts on bighorn sheep, they provide substantial wildlife viewing and hunting opportunities. Seeing mountain goats is the highlight of many road trips along the Beartooth Highway between Red Lodge and Cooke City, Montana. Given their limited allocation, mountain goat hunting licenses are highly sought after, with drawing odds usually around 1.0%. Recently, state-wide mountain goat harvests have averaged about 30 mountain goats per year in Wyoming, 46 mountain goats per year in Idaho, and 180 mountain goats annually in Montana, with 161 of these mountain goats harvested within the Greater Yellowstone Area in 2018. However, in Montana about 86% of the mountain goat harvest currently comes from introduced populations, a complete reversal of situations 50 years ago. (Smith and DeCesare 2017)

## CONCLUSIONS

Both bighorn sheep and mountain goats are fascinating mountain ungulates well adapted to the remote and rugged habitats they occupy. During European settlement of the west, bighorn sheep fared better in the Greater Yellowstone Area than in most places, and although their numbers were reduced, they were never extirpated. Bighorn sheep fared better in rugged, mountainous areas throughout the ecosystem because of the limited areas suitable for agriculture and other major habitat modifying human activities, public ownership of the vast majority of the habitat, and administrative and regulatory statutes such as designated wilderness areas and national parks that emphasize maintaining natural ecosystems and the wildlife that reside in them. As a result of managed hunting, habitat management, and minimizing disease transmission risks from livestock, these herds today are widely distributed throughout the vast wild, mountainous country in the region, and represent some of the largest metapopulations of bighorn sheep currently in existence. Translocation efforts have reestablished some populations

*Moutain goat juvenile, or kid, practicing what it will spend most of its life doing, climbing on rocks. Photo by Mark Gocke.*

that were extirpated, but generally with lackluster results as most populations remain relatively small, and exhibit limited migratory behaviors. Maintaining robust meta-populations of bighorn sheep where they exist is undoubtedly the best approach to the persistence of bighorn sheep on the landscape, as re-creating metapopulations is not easily achieved. Preliminary evidence from the Madison Range of Montana, however, shows promise that inter-range translocations can be used to expand seasonal habitats and migrations of bighorn sheep and perhaps create heterogeneity of behavior and functioning metapopulations while minimizing risk of introducing lethal bacterial pathogens.

Unlike bighorn sheep, mountain goats were not present when the Greater Yellowstone Area was settled by Euro-Americans but were introduced in the last century. They expanded and provide exceptional viewing and hunting opportunities through-out the region but have also created concerns over potential impacts to native bighorn sheep populations in some locations. Acknowledging appreciation of a mountain ungu-late such as the mountain goat, while recognizing and addressing the potential adverse impacts of their expansion is a delicate balancing act. Wildlife managers are familiar with these questions of balance and are often faced with making decisions that consider biological realities and social preferences and tolerances. Making decisions that are bound to be unpopular with some people is to be expected in an arena where so many people care about wildlife and wildlands.

## How We Learn: Translocation of Mountain Ungulates

Recovering populations of locally extirpated wildlife is oftentimes achieved by translocating animals into once occupied, but currently vacant, habitats. The use of this technique is largely how Rocky Mountain bighorn sheep numbers increased in western North America from a low of less than 25,000 animals to approximately 50,000. Sometimes these efforts intentionally place species that did not previously reside in an area into new habitats, expanding their distribution or initiating populations well outside their native ranges, as was the case with mountain goats in numerous western states, including the Greater Yellowstone Area of Idaho and Montana.

The capture and translocation of mountain ungulates is time intensive and very costly, so assessments of potential release sites to ensure the success of the reintroduced (or introduced) population is a necessity. These assessments include habitat evaluations, consideration of competition and disease transmission with existing wildlife populations and domestic animals, and the acceptance or tolerance of landowners if private lands are potentially affected.

Animals must first be captured, which with bighorn sheep and mountain goats is usually done in the winter because they tend to be at lower elevations and more accessible. Snow and colder temperatures also help with heat stress induced by being restrained and handled by humans. Capture operations generally cease prior to the onset of spring, as the stress of capture can be harmful to females in the latter stages of pregnancy. Translocation efforts most often target adult females, as they contribute the most to population increases. Hopefully, the females will be pregnant because giving birth in their new home encourages them to remain in the area and add to the growth of the population. Of course, males are needed for breeding to occur in the new population, but only a handful are needed to serve this purpose.

*The bighorn sheep on the left were captured with a drop net in the Madison Range of Montana and released in the same mountain range to expand the population into suitable, but unused, habitat. The bighorn sheep on the right were captured via helicopter net-gunning, loaded into trailers for transport, and released the next day in an entirely different mountain range in Wyoming. Photos by Richard Horst (upper left), Doug McWhirter, Wyoming Game and Fish Department (upper right), Stan Harter, Wyoming Game and Fish Department (lower right), and Julie Cunningham, Montana Fish, Wildlife and Parks (lower left).*

To minimize the time being handled, every effort is made to release animals as quickly as possible into their new home. Once they are released it is very important to monitor the population to determine if the translocation has been successful or, if not, why. Each effort informs subsequent translocations and hopefully increases the likelihood of the animals thriving in their new landscapes.

The conservation of wildlife rarely occurs without citizens encouraging decision-makers at every level of government to make it a priority. Wildlife management in mixed ownership landscapes such as the Greater Yellowstone Area requires a considerable amount of cooperation, coordination, and compromise. As a result, achieving a balance of biological and social wants and needs is an art as much as science. Ensuring support for wildlife management requires the engagement of many stakeholders and the coordination of many agencies and individuals. This involves meetings among cooperating agencies on items from shared data collection efforts, cooperative research projects, and habitat enhancement projects.

Even though most agencies are guided by statutory and regulatory obligations, much is left up to the desires of the public, who own the wildlife and the lands on which they reside. This requires processes by which the public can express those desires, such as commenting on National Environmental Policy Act (NEPA) documents for federal agency actions such as prescribed burns to improve habitat or industrial development projects that have the potential to negatively impact wildlife habitat. Similarly, state wildlife agencies gather public input on population management objectives and specific hunting season proposals.

*Mountain goat searching for food in Sheepeater Canyon, Yellowstone National Park. Photo by Jacob Frank, National Park Service.*

# REFERENCES

Adams, L. G., and J. A. Bailey. 1982. Population dynamics of mountain goats in the Sawatch Range, Colorado. Journal of Wildlife Management 46:1003-1009.

Adams, L. G., K. L. Risenhoover, and J. A. Bailey. 1982. Ecological relationships of mountain goats and Rocky Mountain bighorn sheep. Biennial Symposium of the Northern Wild Sheep and Goat Council 3:9-22.

Aho, K. A. 2012. Management of introduced mountain goats in Yellowstone National Park: vegetation analysis along a mountain goat gradient. National Park Service, Yellowstone National Park, Mammoth, Wyoming.

Angler. 1883. The big game and the park. Forest and Stream, page 68, February 22.

Auton, A., G. R. Abecasis, D. M. Altshuler, R. M. Durbin, G. R. Abecasis, et al. 2015. A global reference for human genetic variation. Nature 526:68-74.

Avant Courier. 1875. The fur trade [Benton Record]. August 6, Bozeman, Montana.

Avise, J. C. 2000. Phylogeography: the history and formation of species. Harvard University Press, Cambridge, Massachusetts.

Avise, J. C. 2004. Molecular markers, natural history and evolution. Springer Science & Business Media, New York, New York.

Avise, J. C., R. M. Ball, and J. Arnold. 1988. Current versus historical population sizes in vertebrate species with high gene flow: a comparison based on mitochondrial DNA lineages and inbreeding theory for neutral mutations. Molecular Biology and Evolution 5:331-344.

Ayotte, J. B., K. L. Parker, J. M. Arocena, and M. P. Gillingham. 2006. Chemical composition of lick soils: functions of soil ingestion by four ungulate species. Journal of Mammalogy 87:878-888.

Balloux, F., and N. Lugon-Moulin. 2002. The estimation of population differentiation with microsatellite markers. Molecular Ecology 11:155-165.

Baron, J. 2002. Rocky mountain futures: an ecological perspective. Island Press, Washington, D.C.

Barr, C. M., M. Neiman, and D. R. Taylor. 2005. Inheritance and recombination of mitochondrial genomes in plants, fungi and animals. New Phytologist 168:39-50.

Bartlam-Brooks, H. L. A., M. C. Bonyongo, and S. Harris. 2011. Will reconnecting ecosystems allow long-distance mammal migrations to resume? A case study of a zebra *Equus burchelli* migration in Botswana. Oryx 45:210-216.

Besser T. E., E. F. Cassirer, M. A. Highland, P. Wolff, A. Justice-Allen, K. Mansfield, M. A. Davis, and W. J. Foreyt. 2013. Bighorn sheep pneumonia: sorting out the cause of a polymicrobial disease. Preventive Veterinary Medicine 108:85-93.

Besser, T., E. F. Cassirer, K. A. Potter, and W. J. Foreyt. 2017. Exposure of bighorn sheep to domestic goats colonized with *Mycoplasma ovipneumoniae* induces sub-lethal pneumonia. PLoS ONE 16:e0178707.

Besser, T. E., E. F. Cassirer, K. A. Potter, J. VanderSchalie, A. Fischer, D. P. Knowles, D. R. Herndon, F. R. Rurangirwa, G. C. Weiser, S. Srikumaran. 2008. Association of *Mycoplasma ovipneumoniae* infection with population-limiting respiratory disease in free-ranging Rocky Mountain bighorn sheep (*Ovis canadensis canadensis*). Journal of Clinical Microbiology 46:423-430.

Besser, T. E., E. F. Cassirer, C. Yamada, K. A. Potter, C. Herndon, W. J. Foreyt, D. P. Knowles, and S. Srikumaran. 2012a. Survival of bighorn sheep (*Ovis canadensis*) commingled with domestic sheep (*Ovis aries*) in the absence of *Mycoplasma ovipneumoniae*. Journal of Wildlife Diseases 48:168-172.

Besser, T. E., M. A. Highland, K. M. Baker, E. F. Cassirer, N. J. Anderson, J. M. Ramsey, K. G. Mansfield, D. L. Bruning, P. L. Wolff, J. B. Smith, and J. A. Jenks. 2012b. Causes of pneumonia epizootics among bighorn sheep, western United States, 2008-2010. Emerging Infectious Diseases 18:406-414.

Blanchong, J. A., C. A. Anderson, N. J. Clark, R. W. Klaver, P. J. Plummer, M. Cox, C. McAdoo, and P. L. Wolff. 2018. Respiratory disease, behavior, and survival of mountain goat kids. Journal of Wildlife Management 82:1243-1251.

Bleich, V. C., J. D. Wehausen, R. R. Ramey, and J. L. Rechel. 1996. Metapopulation theory and mountain sheep: implication for conservation. Pages 353-373 in D. R. McCullough, editor. Metapopulations and wildlife conservation. Island Press, Washington, D.C.

Bodie, W. L., E. O. Garton, E. R. Taylor, and M. McCoy. 1995. A sightability model for bighorn sheep in canyon habitats. Journal of Wildlife Management 59:832-840.

Brandborg, S. M. 1955. Life history and management of the mountain goat in Idaho. Idaho Wildlife Bulletin 2:1-142.

Brewer, C. E., V. C. Bleich, J. A. Foster, T. Hosch-Hebdon, D. E. McWhirter, E. M. Rominger, M. W. Wagner, and B. P. Wiedmann. 2014. Bighorn sheep: conservation challenges and management strategies for the 21st century. Wild Sheep Working Group, Western Association of Fish and Wildlife Agencies, Cheyenne, Wyoming.

Buechner, H. K. 1960. The bighorn sheep in the United States, its past, present, and future. Wildlife Monographs 4:1-174.

Bunch, T. D., W. Boyce, C. P. Hibler, W. R. Lance, T. R. Spraker, and E. S. Williams. 1999. Diseases of North American wild sheep. Pages 209-237 in R. Valdez and P. R. Krausman, editors. Mountain sheep of North America. University of Arizona Press, Tucson, Arizona.

Bunch, T. D., C. Wu, Y.-P. Zhang, and S. Wang. 2006. Phylogenetic analysis of snow sheep (*Ovis nivicola*) and closely related taxa. Journal of Heredity 97:21-30.

Butler, C. J., W. H. Edwards, J. Jennings-Gaines, H. J. Killion, M. E. Wood, D. E. McWhirter, J. T. Paterson, K. M. Proffitt, E. S. Almberg, P. J. White, J. J. Rotella, and R. A. Garrott. 2017. Assessing respiratory pathogen communities in bighorn sheep populations: sampling realities, challenges, and improvements. PLoS ONE 12:e0180689.

Butler C. J., W. H. Edwards, J. T. Paterson, K. M. Proffitt, J. E. Jennings-Gaines, H. J. Killion, M. E. Wood, J. A. Ramsey, E. S. Almberg, S. R. Dewey, D. E. McWhirter, A. B. Courtemanch, P. J. White, J. J. Rotella, and R. A. Garrott. 2018. Respiratory pathogens and their association with population performance in Montana and Wyoming bighorn sheep populations. PLoS ONE 13:e0207780.

Butler, C. J., R. A. Garrott, and J. J. Rotella. 2013. Correlates of recruitment in Montana bighorn sheep populations. Montana Fish, Wildlife and Parks, Helena, Montana.

Cadsand, B. A. 2012. Response of mountain goats to heliskiing activity: movements and resource selection. Thesis, University of Northern British Columbia, Prince George, British Columbia, Canada.

Cahalane, V. H. 1947. Mammals of North America. Macmillan, New York, New York.

Calfee, H. B. 1899. Calfee's adventures—he and his companion's blood curdling trip to the park over a quarter of a century ago. Bozeman Chronicle, January 5, 1899, Bozeman, Montana.

Carlson, S. M., C. J. Cunningham, and P. A. Westley. 2014. Evolutionary rescue in a changing world. Trends in Ecology & Evolution 29:521-530.

Cassirer, E. F., K. Manlove, E. Almberg, P. Klamath, M. Cox, P. Wolff, A. Roug, J. Shannon, R. Robinson, R. Harris, B. Gonzales, R. Plowright, P. Hudson, P. Cross, A. Dobson, and T. Besser. 2017a. Pneumonia in bighorn sheep: risk and resilience. Journal of Wildlife Management 82:32-45.

Cassirer, E. F., K. R. Manlove, R. K. Plowright, and T. E. Besser. 2017b. Evidence for strain-specific immunity to pneumonia in bighorn sheep. Journal of Wildlife Management 81:133-143.

Cassirer, E. F., R. K. Plowright, K. R. Manlove, P. C. Cross, A. P. Dobson, K. A. Potter, and P. J. Hudson. 2013. Spatio-temporal dynamics of pneumonia in bighorn sheep. Journal of Animal Ecology 82:518-528.

Chadwick, D. H. 1983. A beast the color of winter: the mountain goat observed. University of Nebraska Press, Lincoln, Nebraska.

Chadwick, D. H. 2002. A beast the color of winter: the mountain goat observed. Bison Books, Lincoln, Nebraska.

Chapman, B. B., C. Brönmark, J.-Å. Nilsson, and L.-A. Hansson. 2011. The ecology and evolution of partial migration. Oikos 120:1764-1775.

Colorado Division of Wildlife. 2009. Bighorn sheep-mountain goat interactions. Pages 67-74 in J. L. George, R. Kahn, M. W. Miller, and B. Watkins, editors. Colorado bighorn sheep management plan 2009-2019. DOW-R-S-81-09 ISSN 0084-8875 Special Report No. 81, Colorado Division of Wildlife, Fort Collins, Colorado.

Confederated Salish and Kootenai Tribes. 2005. Fire on the land. Native peoples and fire in the northern Rockies. Fire history project, Pablo, Montana.

Cook, R. C., J. G. Cook, D. L. Murray, P. Zager, B. K. Johnson, and M. W. Gratson. 2001. Development of predictive models of nutritional condition for Rocky Mountain elk. Journal of Wildlife Management 65:973-987.

Cook, R. C., T. R. Stephenson, W. L. Myers, J. G. Cook, and L. A. Shipley. 2007. Validating predictive models of nutritional condition for mule deer. Journal of Wildlife Management 71:1934-1943.

Cooke, P. S. G. 1847-1848. Notes on military reconnaissance from Fort Leavenworth, in Missouri, through the Rocky Mountains to San Diego, California. Subreports from A. R. Johnston and J. W. Abert. U.S. Government Archives, A5:444-501, Washington, D.C.

Côté, S. D., and M. Festa-Bianchet. 2001. Reproductive success in female mountain goats: the influence of maternal age and social rank. Animal Behavior 62:173-181.

Côté, S. D., and M. Festa-Bianchet. 2003. Mountain goat. Pages 1061-1075 in G. A. Feldhamer, B. C. Thompson, and J. A. Chapman, editors. Wild mammals of North America: biology, management, and conservation. Johns Hopkins University Press, Baltimore, Maryland.

Côté, S. D., S. Hamel, A. St. Louis, and J. Mainguy. 2013. Do mountain goats habituate to helicopter disturbance? Journal of Wildlife Management 77:1244-1244.

Courtemanch, A. B. 2014. Seasonal habitat selection and impacts of backcountry recreation on a formerly migratory bighorn sheep population in northwest Wyoming, USA. Thesis, University of Wyoming, Laramie, Wyoming.

Courtemanch, A. B., M. J. Kauffman, S. Kilpatrick, and S. R. Dewey. 2017. Alternative foraging strategies enable a mountain ungulate to persist after migration loss. Ecosphere 8:1-16.

Cullinane Thomas, C., and L. Koontz. 2020. 2019 national park visitor spending effects: Economic contributions to local communities, states, and the nation. Natural Resource Report NPS/NRSS/EQD/NRR—2020/2110. National Park Service, Fort Collins, Colorado.

Cunningham, J., H. Burt, R. Garrott, K. Proffitt, C. Butler, E. Lula, J. Ramsey, and K. Carson. 2018. Evaluating success for an intramountain range transplant of bighorn sheep in southwestern Montana. Proceedings of the Biennial Symposium of the Northern Wild Sheep and Goat Council 21:107-108.

Dailey, T. V., and N. T. Hobbs. 1989. Travel in alpine terrain: energy expenditures for locomotion by mountain goats and bighorn sheep. Canadian Journal of Zoology 67:2368-2375.

Dassanayake, R. P., S. Shanthalingam, R. Subramaniam, C. N. Herndon, J. Bavananthasivam, G. J. Haldorson, W. J. Foreyt, J. F. Evermann, L. M. Herrmann-Hoesing, D. P. Knowles, and S. Srikumaran. 2013. Role of *Bibersteinia trehalosi*, respiratory syncytial virus, and parainfluenza-3 virus in bighorn sheep pneumonia. Veterinary Microbiology 162:166-172.

Davenport, K. M., M. Duan, S. S. Hunter, D. D. New, M. W. Fagnan, M. A. Highland, and B. M. Murdoch. 2018. Complete mitochondrial genome sequence of bighorn sheep. Genome Announcements 6:e00464-18.

DeVoe, J. D. 2015. Occupancy modeling of non-native mountain goats in the Greater Yellowstone Area. Thesis. Montana State University, Bozeman.

DeVoe, J. D., R. A. Garrott, J. J. Rotella, S. R. Challender, P. J. White, M. O'Reilly, and C. J. Butler. 2015. Summer range occupancy modeling of non-native mountain goats in the Greater Yellowstone Area. Ecosphere 6:1-20.

Dingle, H., and V. A. Drake. 2007. What is migration? BioScience 57:113-121.

Doane, G. C. 1875. The buffalo: its ranges and numbers. Bozeman Times, May 11, Bozeman, Montana.

Drummond, J. 1983. Montana sheep trails—a century of progress. Montana Woolgrowers Association, Helena, Montana.

Duffield, J., D. Patterson, and C. Neher. 2000a. Summer 1999 visitor survey, YNP: analysis and results. Draft report prepared for the National Park Service, Denver, Colorado.

Duffield, J., D. Patterson, and C. Neher. 2000b. National telephone survey for attitudes toward management of YNP. Final project report. Bioeconomics, Missoula, Montana.

Dunbar, M. R., W. J. Foreyt, and J. F. Evermann. 1986. Serologic evidence of respiratory syncytial virus infection in free-ranging mountain goats (*Oreamnos americanus*). Journal of Wildlife Diseases 22:415-416.

Dunraven. W. T. W.-Q. 1876. The great divide: travels in the upper Yellowstone in the summer of 1874. Scribner, Welford, and Armstrong, New York, New York.

Eakin, D. H. 2005. Evidence for Shoshonean bighorn sheep trapping and early historic occupation in the Absaroka Mountains of northwest Wyoming. University of Wyoming National Park Service Research Center Annual Report 29:74-86.

Edgar, B., and J. Turnell. 1979. Lady of a legend. Stockade Publishing, Cody, Wyoming.

Ellis, D. H., W. J. L. Sladen, W. A. Lishman, K. R. Clegg, J. W. Duff, G. F. Gee, and J. C. Lewis. 2003. Motorized migrations: the future or mere fantasy? BioScience 53:260-264.

Epps, C. W., P. J. Palsbøll, J. D. Wehausen, G. K. Roderick, R. R. Ramey, and D. R. McCullough. 2005. Highways block gene flow and cause a rapid decline in genetic diversity of desert bighorn sheep: highways reduce genetic diversity. Ecology Letters 8:1029-1038.

Ezenwa, V. O., A. M. Hines, E. A. Archie, E. P. Hoberg, I. M. Asmundsson, and J. T. Hogg. 2010. *Muellerius capillaris* dominates the lungworm community of bighorn sheep at the National Bison Range, Montana. Journal of Wildlife Diseases 46:988-993.

Festa-Bianchet, M. 1988. Seasonal range selection in bighorn sheep: conflicts between forage quality, forage quantity, and predator avoidance. Oecologia 75: 580-586.

Festa-Bianchet, M., and S. D. Côté. 2008. Mountain goats: ecology, behavior, and conservation of an alpine ungulate. Island Press, Washington, D.C.

Festa-Bianchet, M., T. Coulson, J. M. Gaillard, J. T. Hogg, and F. Pelletier. 2006. Stochastic predation events and population persistence in bighorn sheep. Proceedings Royal Society B: Biological Sciences 45:1537-1543.

Finch, T., S. J. Butler, A. M. A. Franco, and W. Cresswell. 2016. Low migratory connectivity is common in long-distance migrant birds. Journal of Animal Ecology 86:662-673.

Fisher, A., and L. Matthews. 2001. The social behaviour of sheep. Pages 211-240 in L. J. Keeling and H. W. Gonyou, editors. Social behavior in farm animals. CABI Publishing, Wallingford, Oxon, UK.

Fitzsimmons, N. N., S. W. Buskirk, and M. H. Smith. 1997. Genetic changes in reintroduced Rocky Mountain bighorn sheep populations. Journal of Wildlife Management 61:863-872.

Flesch, E. P., R. A. Garrott, P. J. White, D. Brimeyer, A. B. Courtemanch, J. A. Cunningham, S. R. Dewey, G. L. Fralick, K. Loveless, D. E. McWhirter, H. Miyasaki, A. Pils, M. A. Sawaya, and S. T. Stewart. 2016. Range expansion and population growth of non-native mountain goats in the Greater Yellowstone Area: challenges for management. Wildlife Society Bulletin 40:241-250.

Flesch, E. P., J. J. Rotella, J. M. Thomson, T. A. Graves, and R. A. Garrott. 2018. Evaluating sample size to estimate genetic management metrics in the genomics era. Molecular Ecology Resources 18:1077-1091.

Flesch, E. P., T. A. Graves, J. M. Thomson, K. M. Proffitt, P. J. White, T. R. Stephenson, and R. A. Garrott. 2020. Evaluating wildlife translocations using genomics: A bighorn sheep case study. Ecology and Evolution 10:13687–13704.

Foreyt, W., E. J. Jenkins, and G. D. Appleyard. 2009. Transmission of lungworms (*Muellerius capilaaris*) from domestic goats to bighorn sheep on common pasture. Journal of Wildlife Diseases 45:272-278.

Forrester, D. J. 1971. Bighorn sheep lungworm-pneumonia complex. Pages 158-173 in J. W. Davis and R. C. Anderson, editors. Parasitic diseases of wild mammals. Iowa State University Press, Ames, Iowa.

Fox, K. A., S. Wootton, S. L. Quackenbush, L. L. Wolfe, I. K. LeVan, M. W. Miller, and T. R. Spraker. 2011. Paranasal sinus masses of Rocky Mountain bighorn sheep (*Ovis canadensis canadensis*). Veterinary Pathology 48:706-712.

Fox, K. A., N. M. Rouse, K. P. Huyvaert, K. A. Griffin, H. J. Killion, J. Jennings-Gaines, W. H. Edwards, S. L. Quackenbush, and M. W. Miller. 2015. Bighorn sheep (*Ovis canadensis*) sinus tumors are associated with coinfections by potentially pathogenic bacteria in the upper respiratory tract. Journal of Wildlife Diseases 51:19-27.

Fox, K. A., S. Wootton, A. Marolf, N. Rouse, I. LeVan, T. Spraker, M. Miller, and S. Quackenbush. 2016. Experimental transmission of bighorn sheep sinus tumors to bighorn sheep (*Ovis canadensis canadensis*) and domestic sheep. Veterinary Pathology 53:1164-1171

Francois, O., M. Currat, N. Ray, E. Han, L. Excoffier, and J. Novembre. 2010. Principal component analysis under population genetic models of range expansion and admixture. Molecular Biology and Evolution 27:1257-1268.

Frankham, R. 2007. Effective population size/adult population size ratios in wildlife: a review. Genetics Research 89:491-503.

Frankham, R., J. D. Ballou, and D. A. Briscoe. 2010. Introduction to conservation genetics. Cambridge University Press, Cambridge, UK.

Frankham, R., J. D. Ballou, K. Ralls, M. D. B. Eldridge, M. Dubash, C. B. Fenster, R. C. Lacy, and P. Sunnucks. 2017. Genetic management of fragmented animal and plant populations. Oxford University Press, Oxford, UK.

Frison, G. C. 2004. Survival by hunting: prehistoric human predators and animal prey. University of California Press, Berkeley and Los Angeles, California.

Fryxell, J. M., J. Greever, and A. R. E. Sinclair. 1988. Why are migratory ungulates so abundant? American Naturalist 131:781-798.

Fryxell, J. M., and A. R. E. Sinclair. 1988. Causes and consequences of migration by large herbivores. Trends in Ecology and Evolution 3:237-241.

Gaillard, J.-M., M. Festa-Bianchet, N. G. Yoccoz, A. Loison, and C. Toïgo. 2000. Temporal variation in fitness components of population dynamics of large herbivores. Annual Review of Ecology and Systematics 31:367-393.

Garrett, R., and C. M. Grisham. 2013. Biochemistry. Brooks/Cole, Belmont, California.

Geist, V. 1964. On the rutting behavior of the mountain goat. Journal of Mammalogy 45:551-568.

Geist, V. 1967. On fighting injuries and dermal shields of mountain goats. Journal of Wildlife Management 31:192-194.

Geist, V. 1971. Mountain sheep: a study in behavior and evolution. University of Chicago Press, Chicago, Illinois.

Giacometti, M., M. Janovsky, H. Jenny, J. Nicolet, L. Belloy, E. Goldschmidt-Clermont, and J. Frey. 2002. *Mycoplasma conjuctivitae* infection is not maintained in alpine chamois in eastern Switzerland. Journal of Wildlife Diseases 38:297-304.

Gill, R. B. 2010. To save a mountain lion: evolving philosophy of nature and cougars. Pages 5-16 in M. Hornocker and S. Negri, editors. Cougar ecology and conservation. University of Chicago Press, Chicago, Illinois.

Gilroy, J. J., J. A. Gill, S. H. M. Butchart, V. R. Jones, and A. M. A. Franco. 2016. Migratory diversity predicts population declines in birds. Ecology Letters 19:308-317.

Glasgow, W. M., T. C. Sorensen, H. D. Carr, and K. G. Smith. 2003. Management plan for mountain goats in Alberta. Alberta Fish and Wildlife, Edmonton, Alberta, Canada.

Gonzalez-Voyer, A., M. Festa-Bianchet, and K. G. Smith. 2001. Efficiency of aerial surveys of mountain goats. Wildlife Society Bulletin 29:140-144.

Gross, J. E. 2001. Evaluating effects of an expanding mountain goat population on native bighorn sheep: a simulation model of competition and disease. Biological Conservation 101:171-185.

Hall, L. S., P. R. Krausman, and M. L. Morrison. 1997. The habitat concept and a plea for standard terminology. Wildlife Society Bulletin 25:173-182.

Hamada, H., M. G. Petrino, T. Kakunaga, M. Seidman, and B. D. Stollar. 1984. Characterization of genomic poly (dT-dG). poly (dC-dA) sequences: structure, organization, and conformation. Molecular and Cellular Biology 4:2610-2621.

Hansen, J., M. Sato, R. Ruedy, K. Lo, D. W. Lea, and M. Medina-Elizade. 2006. Global temperature change. Proceedings of the National Academy Sciences USA 103:14288-14293.

Hanski, I. 1999. Metapopulation ecology. Oxford University Press, Oxford, UK.

Harris, M. 1889. Report of the Superintendent of the Yellowstone National Park to the Secretary of the Interior, 1889. Government Printing Office, Washington, D.C.

Haroldson, M. A., C. C. Schwartz, K. C. Kendall, K. A. Gunther, D. S. Moody, K. Frey, and D. Paetkau. 2010. Genetic analysis of individual origins supports isolation of grizzly bears in the Greater Yellowstone Ecosystem. Ursus 21:1-13.

Hawkes, L. E. 1976. USDA Forest Service environmental analysis report (with appendix), High Absaroka sheep range. Gallatin National Forest, Bozeman, Montana.

Hayden, J. A. 1984. Introduced mountain goats in the Snake River Range, Idaho. Biennial Symposium of the Northern Wild Sheep and Goat Council 4:94-119.

Hebert, D. M. 1978. A systems approach to mountain goat management. Biennial Symposium of the Northern Wild Sheep and Goat Council 2:227-243.

Hebert, D. M., and I. M. Cowan. 1971. Natural salt licks as a part of the ecology of the mountain goat. Canadian Journal of Zoology 49:605-610.

Hebert, D. M., and H. D. Langin. 1982. Mountain goat inventory and harvest strategies: a reevaluation. Biennial Symposium of the Northern Wild Sheep and Goat Council 3:339-350.

Hebert, D. M., and W. G. Turnbull. 1977. A description of southern interior and coastal mountain goat ecotypes in British Columbia. Pages 126-146 in W. Samuel and W. G. Macgregor, editors. Proceedings of the first international mountain goat symposium. Kalispell, Montana.

Hedrick, P. W., G. A. Gutierrez-Espeleta, and R. N. Lee. 2001. Founder effect in an island population of bighorn sheep. Molecular Ecology 10:851-857.

Helfield, J. M., and R. J. Naiman. 2001. Effects of salmon-derived nitrogen on riparian forest growth and implications for stream productivity. Environmental Sciences Faculty and Staff Publications, 19. https://cedar.wwu.edu/esci_facpubs/19.

Historical Research Associates. 2006a. Crow use rights in the Yellowstone, Grand Teton, and National Elk Refuge areas: narrative report. Prepared for the National Park Service by Ian Smith, Research Historian, and Emily Greenwald, Project Manager, Missoula, Montana.

Historical Research Associates. 2006b. Eastern Shoshone use rights in the Yellowstone, Grand Teton, and National Elk Refuge areas: narrative report. Prepared for the National Park Service by Diane Krahe, Research Historian, Ian Smith, Research Historian, and Emily Greenwald, Project Manager, Missoula, Montana.

Historical Research Associates. 2006c. Shoshone-Bannock use rights in the Yellowstone, Grand Teton, and National Elk Refuge areas: narrative report. Prepared for the National Park Service by Ian Smith, Research Historian, and Emily Greenwald, Project Manager, Missoula, Montana.

Hogg, J. T., S. H. Forbes, B. M. Steele, and G. Luikart. 2006. Genetic rescue of an insular population of large mammals. Proceedings of the Royal Society B: Biological Sciences 273:1491-1499.

Holm, B. 1982. On making horn bows. Pages 116-130 in T. M. Hamilton, Appendix I. Native American bows. Special publication number 5, Missouri Archaeological Society, Columbia, Missouri.

Holroyd, J. C. 1967. Observations of Rocky Mountain goats on Mount Wardle, Kootenay National Park, British Columbia. Canadian Field Naturalist 81:1-22.

Honess, R. F., and N. M. Frost. 1942. A Wyoming bighorn sheep study: Pittman-Robertson Project Wyoming 13-R. Wyoming Game and Fish Department Bulletin No. 1, Cheyenne, Wyoming.

Hooker, P. 2011. Images of America: Columbus and Stillwater County. Arcadia Publishing, Mount Pleasant, South Carolina.

Hopkins, A., J. P. Fitzgerald, A. Chappell, and G. Byrne. 1992. Population dynamics and behavior of mountain goats using Elliott Ridge, Gore Range, Colorado. Biennial Symposium of the Northern Wild Sheep and Goat Council 8:340-356.

Houston, D. B., and E. G. Schreiner. 1995. Alien species in national parks: drawing lines in space and time. Conservation Biology 9:204-209.

Houston, D. B., E. G. Schreiner, and B. B. Moorhead. 1994. Mountain goats in Olympic National Park: biology and management of an introduced species. US-DI-NPS Scientific Monograph NPS/NROLYM/NRSM-94/25, Denver, Colorado.

Howe, D. L., G. T. Woods, and G. Marquis. 1966. Infection of bighorn sheep (*Ovis canadensis*) with myxovirus parainfluenza-3 and other respiratory viruses. Results of serologic tests and culture of nasal swabs and lung tissue. Bulletin of the Wildlife Disease Association 2:34-37.

Hunter, R. F., and C. Milner. 1963. The behaviour of individual, related and groups of South Country Cheviot Hill sheep. Animal Behaviour 11:507-513.

Hurley, K. 1985. The Trout Peak bighorn sheep herd, northwestern Wyoming. Thesis, University of Wyoming, Laramie, Wyoming.

Hurley, K. P., and K. M. Firchow. 1994. South Absaroka/Owl Creek Mountains bighorn sheep study: final report, August 1994. Wyoming Game and Fish Department, Cheyenne, Wyoming.

Idaho Department of Fish and Game. 2010. Bighorn sheep management plan 2010. Idaho Department of Fish and Game, Boise, Idaho.

Idaho Department of Fish and Game. 2019. Mountain goat management plan 2019. Idaho Department of Fish and Game, Boise, Idaho.

Jakopak, R. P., T. N. Lasharr, S. P. Dwinnell, G. L. Fralick, and K. L. Monteith. 2019. Rapid acquisition of memory in a complex landscape by a mule deer. Ecology e02854.

Janovsky M., J. Frey, J. Nicolet, L. Belloy, E. Goldschmidt-Clermont, and M. Giacometti. 2001. *Mycoplasma conjunctivae* is self-maintained in the Swiss domestic sheep population. Veterinary Microbiology 83:11-22.

Jesmer, B. R., J. A. Merkle, J. R. Goheen, E. O. Aikens, J. L. Beck, A. B. Courtemanch, M. A. Hurley, D. E. McWhirter, H. M. Miyasaki, K. L. Monteith, and M. J. Kauffman. 2018. Is ungulate migration culturally transmitted? Evidence of social learning from translocated animals. Science 361:1023-1025.

Johnson, H. E., L. S. Mills, T. R. Stephenson, and J. D. Wehausen. 2010. Population-specific vital rate contributions influence management of an endangered ungulate. Ecological Applications 20:1753-1765.

Johnson, R. L. 1977. Distribution, abundance and management status of mountain goats in North America. Pages 1-7 in W. Samuel and W. G. Macgregor, editors. Proceedings of the first international mountain goat symposium. Kalispell, Montana.

Joslin, G. 1986. Mountain goat population changes in relation to energy exploration along Montana's Rocky Mountain Front. Biennial Symposium North American Wild Sheep and Goat Council 5:253-271.

Kamath, P. L., K. Manlove, E. F. Cassirer, P. C. Cross, and T. E. Besser. 2019. Genetic structure of *Mycoplasma ovipneumoniae* informs pathogen spillover dynamics between domestic and wild *Caprinae* in the western United States. Scientific Reports 9:1-14.

Kim, S., and A. Misra. 2007. SNP genotyping: technologies and biomedical applications. Annual review of Biomedical Engineering 9:289.

Kornfeld, M., G. C. Frison, and M. L. Larson. 2010. Prehistoric hunter-gatherers of the high plains and Rockies. Left Coast Press, Walnut Creek, California.

Krausman, P. R., and R. T. Bowyer. 2003. Mountain sheep (*Ovis canadensis* and *O. dalli*). Pages 1095-1115 in G. A. Feldhamer, B. C. Thompson, and J. A. Chapman, editors. Wild mammals of North America: biology, management, and conservation. Johns Hopkins University Press, Baltimore, Maryland.

Kuck, L. 1977. The impact of hunting on Idaho's Pahsimeroi mountain goat herd. Pages 114-125 in W. Samuel and W. G. Macgregor, editors. Proceedings of the first international mountain goat symposium. Kalispell, Montana.

Laundré, J. W. 1990. The status, distribution, and management of mountain goats in the Greater Yellowstone Ecosystem. NPS Order # PX 1200-8-0828. Yellowstone National Park, Mammoth, Wyoming.

Laundré, J. W. 1994. Resource overlap between mountain goats and bighorn sheep. Great Basin Naturalist 54:114-121.

Laws, R. M. 1981. Experiences in the study of large mammals. Pages 19-45 in C. W. Fowler and T. S. Smith, editors. Dynamics of large mammal populations. Wiley, New York, New York.

Lee, C. M., and K. Puseman. 2017. Ice patch hunting in the Greater Yellowstone Area, Rocky Mountains, USA: wood shafts, chipped stone projectile points, and bighorn sheep (*Ovis canadensis*). American Antiquity 82:223-243.

Lemke, T. O. 2004. Origin, expansion, and status of mountain goats in Yellowstone National Park. Wildlife Society Bulletin 32:532-541.

Lentfer, J. W. 1955. A two-year study of the Rocky Mountain goat in the Crazy Mountains, Montana. Journal of Wildlife Management 19:417-429.

Lewis, D. S. 2008. Yellowstone's Sheep Eater Indians. Living among the powerful spirits. Montana Pioneer, July.

Longshore, K. M., C. Lowrey, and D. B. Thompson. 2009. Compensating for diminishing natural water: predicting the impacts of water development on summer habitat of desert bighorn sheep. Journal of Arid Environments 73:280-286.

Love Stowell, S. M., R. B. Gagne, D. E. McWhirter, H. Edwards, and H. B. Ernest. 2020. Bighorn sheep genetic structure reflects geography and management. Journal of Wildlife Management 84:1072-1090.

Lowrey, B. L., C. J. Butler, W. H. Edwards, M. E. Wood, S. R. Dewey, G. L. Fralick, J. Jennings-Gaines, H. Killion, D. E. McWhirter, H. M. Miyasaki, S. T. Steward, K. S. White, P. J. White, and R. A. Garrott. 2018a. A survey of bacterial respiratory pathogens in native and introduced mountain goats (*Oreamnos americanus*). Journal of Wildlife Diseases 54:852-858.

Lowrey, B., R. A. Garrott, D. E. McWhirter, P. J. White, N. J. DeCesare, and S. T. Stewart. 2018b. Niche similarities among introduced and native mountain ungulates. Ecological Applications 28:1131-1142.

Lowrey, B., R. A. Garrott, H. M. Miyasaki, G. Fralick, and S. R. Dewey. 2017. Seasonal resource selection by introduced mountain goats in the southwest Greater Yellowstone Area. Ecosphere 8:1-20.

Lowrey, B., K. M. Proffitt, D. E. McWhirter, P. J. White, A. B. Courtemanch, S. R. Dewey, H. M. Miyasaki, K. L. Monteith, J. S. Mao, J. L. Grigg, C. J. Butler, E. S. Lula and R. A. Garrott. 2019. Characterizing population and individual migration patterns among native and restored bighorn sheep (*Ovis canadensis*). Ecology and Evolution 9:8829-8839.

Lula, E. S., B. Lowrey, K. M. Proffitt, A. R. Litt, J. A. Cunningham, C. J. Butler, and R. A. Garrott. 2020. Is habitat constraining bighorn sheep restoration: a case study. Journal of Wildlife Management 84:588-600.

Lunt, D. H., L. E. Whipple, and B. C. Hyman. 1998. Mitochondrial DNA variable number tandem repeats (VNTRs): utility and problems in molecular ecology. Molecular Ecology 7:1441-1455.

Manni, M. F., M. Littlejohn, J. Evans, J. Gramann, and S. J. Hollenhorst. 2007. Yellowstone National Park visitor study, summer 2006. Park Studies Unit, Visitor Services Project, Report 178. USDI, NPS, Washington, D.C.

McIntyre, C. L., and C. Ellis. 2011. Landscape dynamics in the Greater Yellowstone Area. Natural Resource Technical Report NPS/GRYN/NRTR-2011/506. National Park Service, Fort Collins, Colorado.

McWhirter, D. 2004. Mountain goat status and management in Wyoming. Biennial Symposium Northern Wild Sheep and Goat Council 14:101-113.

Meagher, M. M., and D. B. Houston. 1998. Yellowstone and the biology of time. Photographs across a century. University of Oklahoma Press, Norman, Oklahoma.

Meagher, M., W. J. Quinn, and L. Stackhouse. 1992. Chlamydial-caused infectious keratoconjunctivitis in bighorn sheep of Yellowstone National Park. Journal of Wildlife Diseases 28:171-176.

Merkle, J. A., H. Sawyer, K. L. Monteith, S. P. H. Dwinnell, G. L. Fralick, and M. J. Kauffman. 2019. Spatial memory shapes migration and its benefits: evidence from a large herbivore. Ecology Letters doi.org/10.1111/ele.13362.

Metz, M. C., D. W. Smith, J. A. Vucetich, D. R. Stahler, and R. O. Peterson. 2012. Seasonal patterns of predation for gray wolves in the multi-prey system of Yellowstone National Park. Journal of Animal Ecology 81:553-563.

Miller, D. S., E. Hoberg, G. Weise, K. Aune, M. Atkinson, and C. Kimberling. 2012. A review of hypothesized determinants associated with bighorn sheep (*Ovis canadensis*) die-offs. Veterinary Medicine International 2012:1-19.

Miller, D. S., G. C. Weiser, K. Aune, B. Roeder, M. Atkinson, N. Anderson, T. J. Roffe, K. A. Keating, P. L. Chapman, C. Kimberling, and J. Rhyan. 2011. Shared bacterial and viral respiratory agents in bighorn sheep (*Ovis canadensis*), domestic sheep (*Ovis aries*), and goats (*Capra hircus*) in Montana. Veterinary Medicine International 2011.

Miller, J. M., S. S. Moore, P. Stothard, X. Liao, and D. W. Coltman. 2015. Harnessing cross-species alignment to discover SNPs and generate a draft genome sequence of a bighorn sheep (*Ovis canadensis*). BMC Genomics 16:397.

Miller, M. W., J. E. Vayhinger, D. C. Bowden, S. P. Roush, T. E. Verry, A. N. Torres, and V. D. Jurgens. 2000. Drug treatment for lungworm in bighorn sheep: reevaluation of a 20-year-old management prescription. Journal of Wildlife Management 64:505-512.

Mincher, B. J., R. D. Ball, T. P. Houghton, J. Mionczynski, and P. A. Hnilicka. 2008. Some aspects of geophagia in Wyoming bighorn sheep (*Ovis canadensis*). European Journal of Wildlife Research 54:193-198.

Mistretta, A. M. 2012. The Mountain Shoshone – a history of the Sheep Eater Indians in the Big Sky area. Montana Outlaw Magazine, Summer.

Monello, R. J., D. L. Murray, and E. F. Cassirer. 2001. Ecological correlates of pneumonia epizootics in bighorn sheep herds. Canadian Journal of Zoology 79:1423-1432.

Montana Fish, Wildlife and Parks. 2010. Montana bighorn sheep conservation strategy. Helena, Montana.

Muschenheim, A. L., E. T. Thorne, E. S. Williams, S. H. Anderson, and F. C. Wright. 1990. Psoroptic scabies in Rocky Mountain bighorn sheep (*Ovis canadensis canadensis*) from Wyoming. Journal of Wildlife Diseases 26:554-557.

Nabokov, P., and L. Loendorf. 2004. Restoring a presence: American Indians and Yellowstone National Park. University of Oklahoma Press, Norman, Oklahoma.

National Park Service. 2006. Management policies. U.S. Department of Interior, National Park Service. U.S. Government Printing Office, Washington, D.C.

National Park Service. 2016. Dinosaur National Monument protocol for Rocky Mountain goat restriction and removal. <https://parkplanning.nps.gov/documentsList.cfm?parkID=50&projectID=55971>.

National Park Service. 2018a. Final mountain goat management plan/environmental impact statement. U.S. Department of the Interior, Olympic National Park, Port Angeles, Washington. <https://parkplanning.nps.gov/showFile.cfm?projectID=49246&MIMEType=application%2Fpdf&filename=OLYM%20Goat%20FEIS%2Epdf&sfid=324115>. Accessed 28 May 2019

National Park Service. 2018b. Mountain goat management plan environmental assessment. U.S. Department of the Interior, Grand Teton National Park, Moose, Wyoming. <http://parkplanning.nps.gov/mountaingoat>. Accessed March 1, 2018.

National Wildlife Federation. 2018. Adopt a wildlife acre program. <https://nwf.org/Our-Work/Our-Lands/Adopt-a-Wildlife-Acre.> Accessed February 13, 2018.

Nei, M., and S. Kumar. 2000. Molecular evolution and phylogenetics. Oxford University Press, Oxford, UK.

Nei, M., T. Maruyama, and R. Chakraborty. 1975. The bottleneck effect and genetic variability in populations. Evolution 29:1-10.

Norris, P. W. 1878. Report upon the Yellowstone National Park to the Secretary of the Interior by P. W. Norris, Superintendent, for the year 1877. U.S. Government Printing Office, Washington, D.C. <http://mtmemory.org/cdm/ref/collection/p16013coll95/id/235>.

N. V. S. 1872. From the Yellowstone. December 10 letter from Sheffer's Ranch, Yellowstone Valley. December 12 issue of the Avant Courier newspaper, Bozeman, Montana.

O'Brien, J. M., C. S. O'Brien, C. McCarthy, and T. E. Carpenter. 2014. Incorporating foray behavior into models estimating contact risk between bighorn sheep and areas occupied by domestic sheep. Wildlife Society Bulletin 38:321-331.

Olivieri, A., A. Achilli, M. Pala, V. Battaglia, S. Fornarino, N. Al-Zahery, R. Scozzari, F. Cruciani, D. M. Behar, J.-M. Dugoujon, C. Coudray, A. S. Santachiara-Benerecetti, O. Semino, H.-J. Bandelt, and A. Torroni. 2006. The mtDNA legacy of the Levantine Early Upper Palaeolithic in Africa. Science 314:1767-1770.

Olson, Z. H., D. G. Whittaker, and O. E. Rhodes. 2013. Translocation history and genetic diversity in reintroduced bighorn sheep. Journal of Wildlife Management 77:1553-1563.

Oreamnos americanus (ID 17040) - Genome - NCBI. (n.d.). . https://www.ncbi.nlm.nih.gov/genome/?term=mountain+goat.

Organ, J. F., V. Geist, S. P. Mahoney, S. Williams, P. R. Krausman, G. R. Batcheller, T. A. Decker, R. Carmichael, P. Nanjappa, R. Regan, R. A. Medellin, R. Cantu, R. E. McCabe, S. Craven, G. M. Vecellio, and D. J. Decker. 2012. The North American model of wildlife conservation. Technical Review 12-04. The Wildlife Society, Bethesda, Maryland.

*Ovis aries* Annotation Report. 2015. https://www.ncbi.nlm.nih.gov/genome/annotation_euk/Ovis_aries/102/.

*Ovis canadensis* (ID 10514) - Genome - NCBI. (n.d.). https://www.ncbi.nlm.nih.gov/genome/10514?genome_assembly_id=437948.

Parks, J. B., and J. J. England. 1974. A serological survey for selected viral infections of Rocky Mountain bighorn sheep. Journal of Wildlife Diseases 10:107-110.

Pederson, G. T., L. J. Graumlich, D. B. Fagre, T. Kipfer, C. C. Muhlfeld. 2010. A century of climate and ecosystem change in western Montana: what do temperature trends portend? Climate Change 98:133-154.

Pettorelli, N., S. Ryan, T. Muller, N. Bunnefeld, B. Jedrzejewska, M. Lima, and K. Kausrud. 2011. The normalized difference vegetation index (NDVI): unforeseen successes in animal ecology. Climate Research 46:15-27.

Picton, H. D., and T. N. Lonner. 2008. Montana's wildlife legacy: decimation to restoration. Media Works Publishing, Bozeman, Montana.

Pioneer Society of Sweet Grass County. 2008. Pioneer memories II. Pioneer Publishing Company, Big Timber, Montana.

Poissant, J., J. T. Hogg, C. S. Davis, J. M. Miller, J. F. Maddox, and D. W. Coltman. 2010. Genetic linkage map of a wild genome: genomic structure, recombination and sexual dimorphism in bighorn sheep. BMC Genomics 11:524.

Poole, K. G., K. D. Bachmann, and I. E. Teske. 2010. Mineral lick use by GPS radio-collared mountain goats in southeastern British Columbia. Western North American Naturalist 70:208-217.

Poole, K. G., and D. C. Heard. 2003. Seasonal habitat use and movements of mountain goats, *Oreamnos americanus,* in east-central British Columbia. Canadian Field-Naturalist 117:565-576.

Poole, K. G., K. Stuart-Smith, and I. E. Teske. 2009. Wintering strategies by mountain goats in interior mountains. Canadian Journal of Zoology 87:273-283.

Portier, C., M. Festa-Bianchet, J.-M. Gaillard, J. T. Jorgenson, and N. G. Yoccoz. 1998. Effects of density and weather on survival of bighorn sheep lambs (*Ovis canadensis*). Journal of Zoology 245:271-278.

Post, G. 1962. Pasteurellosis of Rocky Mountain bighorn sheep (*Ovis canadensis canadensis*). Wildlife Disease 23:1-14.

Pritchard, J. K., M. Stephens, and P. Donnelly. 2000. Inference of population structure using multilocus genotype data. Genetics 155:945-959.

Proffitt, K. M., A. B. Courtemanch, S. R. Dewey, B. Lowrey, D. E. McWhirter, K. L. Monteith, J. T. Paterson, J. Rotella, P. J. White, and R. A. Garrott. 2021. Regional variability in Rocky Mountain bighorn sheep pregnancy and survival rates. Ecosphere, 2:e03410

Quintana-Murci, L., O. Semino, H.-J. Bandelt, G. Passarino, K. McElreavey, and A. S. Santachiara-Benerecetti. 1999. Genetic evidence of an early exit of Homo sapiens sapiens from Africa through eastern Africa. Nature Genetics 23:437-441.

Raj, A., M. Stephens, and J. K. Pritchard. 2014. fastSTRUCTURE: variational inference of population structure in large SNP data sets. Genetics 197:573-589.

Reed, D. F. 1986. Alpine habitat selection in sympatric mountain goats and mountain sheep. Northern Wild Sheep and Goat Council 5:421-422.

Reed, D. F. 2001. A conceptual interference competition model for introduced mountain goats. Journal of Wildlife Management 65:125-128.

Reed, D. H., and R. Frankham. 2003. Correlation between fitness and genetic diversity. Conservation Biology 17:230-237.

Reference, G. H. 2019. What are single nucleotide polymorphisms (SNPs)? https://ghr.nlm.nih.gov/primer/genomicresearch/snp.

Reich, D., A. L. Price, and N. Patterson. 2008. Principal component analysis of genetic data. Nature Genetics 40:491-492.

Resource Systems Group. 2017. Yellowstone National Park visitor use study: summer, 2016. White River Junction, Vermont.

Rice, C. G. 2008. Seasonal altitudinal movements of mountain goats. Journal of Wildlife Management 72:1706-1716.

Rice, C. G., K. J. Jenkins, and W. Chang. 2009. A sightability model for mountain goats. Journal of Wildlife Management 73:468-478.

Rideout, C. 1974. A radio telemetry study of the ecology and behavior of the mountain goat in western Montana. Dissertation, University of Kansas, Lawrence, Kansas.

Riley, S., W. Siemer, D. Decker, L. Carpenter, J. Organ, and L. Berchielli. 2003. Adaptive impact management: an integrative approach to wildlife management. Human Dimensions Wildlife 8:81-95.

Risenhoover, K. L., and J. A. Bailey. 1985. Foraging ecology of mountain sheep: implications for habitat management. Journal of Wildlife Management 49:797-804.

Rocky Mountain Elk Foundation and Conservation Visions. 2006. Opportunity for all. The story of the north American model for wildlife conservation. Missoula, Montana.

Rominger, E. M., H. A. Whitlaw, D. L. Weybright, W. C. Dunn, and W. B. Ballard. 2004. The influence of mountain lion predation on bighorn sheep translocations. Journal of Wildlife Management 68:993-999.

Rush, W. M. 1927. Notes on diseases in wild game animals. Journal of Mammalogy 8:163-165.

Rush, W. M. 1933. Northern Yellowstone elk study. Montana Fish and Game Commission. Missoulian Publishing Company, Missoula, Montana.

Ryder, T. J., and R. P. Lanka. 1997. History and current status of Rocky Mountain bighorn sheep in the southern Wind River mountains, Wyoming: final project report. Wyoming Game and Fish Department, Lander, Wyoming.

Ryder T. J., E. S. Williams, K. W. Mills, K. H. Bowles, and E. T. Thorne. 1992. Effect of pneumonia on population size and lamb recruitment in Whiskey Mountain bighorn sheep. Pages 136-146 in Proceedings of the Eighth Biennial Symposium of the Northern Wild Sheep and Goat Council, Cody, Wyoming.

Saccheri, I., M. Kuussaari, M. Kankare, P. Vikman, W. Fortelius, and I. Hanski. 1998. Inbreeding and extinction in a butterfly metapopulation. Nature 392:491.

Sagaff, M. 2005. Do non-native species threaten the natural environment? Journal of Agriculture and Environmental Ethics 18:215-236.

Samson, J., J. C. Holmes, J. T. Jorgenson, and W. D. Wishart. 1987. Experimental infections of free-ranging Rocky Mountain bighorn sheep with lungworms (*Protostrongylus spp.*; *Nematoda: Protostrongylidae*). Journal of Wildlife Diseases 23:396-403.

Samuel, W. M., G. A. Chalmers, J. G. Stelfox, A. Loewen, and J. J. Thomsen. 1975. Contagious ecthyma in bighorn sheep and mountain goat in western Canada. Journal of Wildlife Diseases 11:26-31.

Sawyer, H., and F. Lindzey. 2002. A review of predation on bighorn sheep (*Ovis canadensis*). Wyoming Cooperative Fish and Wildlife Research Unit, University of Wyoming, Laramie, Wyoming.

Schindler, D. E., J. B. Armstrong, and T. E. Reed. 2015a. The portfolio concept in ecology and evolution. Frontiers in Ecology and the Environment 13:257-263.

Schindler, D. E., R. Hilborn, B. Chasco, C. P. Boatright, T. P. Quinn, L. A. Rogers, and M. S. Webster. 2015b. Population diversity and the portfolio effect in an exploited species. Nature 465:609-613.

Schommer, T. J., and M. M. Woolever. 2008. A review of disease related conflicts between domestic sheep and goats and bighorn sheep. General Technical Report RMRS-GTR-209. U.S. Department of Agriculture, Forest Service, Rocky Mountain Research Station, Fort Collins, Colorado.

Schullery, P., and L. Whittlesey. 2001. Mountain goats in the Greater Yellowstone Ecosystem: a prehistoric and historical context. Western North American Naturalist 61:289-307.

Sells, S. N, M. S. Mitchell, J. J. Nowak, P. M. Lukacs, N. J. Anderson, J. M. Ramsey, J. A. Gude, and P. R. Krausman. 2015. Modeling risk of pneumonia epizootics in bighorn sheep. Journal of Wildlife Management 79:195-210.

Seton, E. T. 1929. Lives of game animals. Doubleday Page and Company, New York, New York.

Shanthalingam, S., S. Narayanan, S. A. Batra, B. Jegarubee, and S. Srikumaran. 2016. *Fusobacterium necrophorum* in North American bighorn sheep (*Ovis canadensis*) pneumonia. Journal of Wildlife Diseases 52:616-620.

Simberloff, D. 2005. Non-native species DO threaten the natural environment! Journal of Agriculture and Environmental Ethics 18:595-607.

Singer, F. J., and J. L. Doherty. 1985. Movements and habitat use in an unhunted population of mountain goats, *Oreamnos americanus*. Canadian Field Naturalist 99:205-217.

Singer, F. J., and M. A. Gudorf. 1999. Restoration of bighorn sheep metapopulations in and near 15 national parks: conservation of a severely fragmented species. U.S. Geological Survey Open File Report 99-102, Midcontinent Ecological Science Center, Fort Collins, Colorado.

Singer, F. J., C. M. Papouchis, and K. K. Symonds. 2000. Translocations as a tool for restoring populations of bighorn sheep. Restoration Ecology 8:6-13.

Skalski, J. R., K. E. Ryding, and J. J. Millspaugh. 2005. Wildlife demography: analysis of sex, age, and count data. Elsevier Academic Press, San Diego, California.

Skinner, M. P. 1926. Mountain goat (*Oreamnos montanus missoulae*) not found in Wyoming. Journal of Mammalogy 7:334-335.

Slabach, B. L., T. B. Corey, J. R. Aprille, P. T. Starks, and B. Dane. 2015. Geophagic behavior in mountain goats (*Oreamnos americanus*): support for meeting metabolic demands. Canadian Journal of Zoology 93:599-604.

Smith, B. L. 1982. The history, current status and management of bighorn sheep on Wind River Indian Reservation. U.S. Fish and Wildlife Service, Lander, Wyoming.

Smith, B. L., and N. J. DeCesare. 2017. Status of Montana's mountain goats: a synthesis of management data (1960-2015) and field biologist perspectives. Final report, Montana Fish, Wildlife and Parks, Missoula, Montana.

Smith, J. B., T. W. Grovenburg, and J. A. Jenks. 2015. Parturition and bed site selection of bighorn sheep at local and landscape scales. Journal of Wildlife Management 79:393-401.

Smith, P. 2002. Montana Sweet Grass country: from Melville to Boulder River Valley. Sweet Grass Museum Society, Crazy Mountain Museum, Big Timber, Montana.

Smith, T. B., M. T. Kinnison, S. Y. Strauss, T. L. Fuller, and S. P. Carroll. 2014. Prescriptive evolution to conserve and manage biodiversity. Annual Review of Ecology, Evolution, and Systematics 45:1-22.

Smith, T. S., P. J. Hardin, and J. T. Flinders. 1999. Response of bighorn sheep to clear-cut logging and prescribed burning. Wildlife Society Bulletin 27:840-845.

Spraker, T. R., J. K. Collins, W. J. Adrian, and J. H. Otterman. 1986. Isolation and serologic evidence of a respiratory syncytial virus in bighorn sheep from Colorado. Journal of Wildlife Diseases 22:416-418.

Stewart, S. T. 1975. Ecology of the West Rosebud and Stillwater bighorn sheep herds, Beartooth Mountains, Montana. Thesis, Montana State University, Bozeman, Montana.

Stewart, S. T. 1982. Late parturition in bighorn sheep. Journal of Mammalogy 63:154-155.

Stryker, L. P. 2009. Images of America: Big Timber. Arcadia Publishing, Mount Pleasant, South Carolina.

Taylor, S., and K. Brunt. 2007. Winter habitat use by mountain goats in the Kingcome River drainage of coastal British Columbia. Journal of Ecosystems and Management 8:30-48.

Toweill, D. E., and V. Geist. 1999. Return of royalty: wild sheep of North America. Boone and Crockett Club and the Foundation for North American Wild Sheep, Missoula, Montana.

Toweill, D. E., S. Gordon, E. Jenkins, T. Kreeger, and D. McWhirter. 2004. A working hypothesis for the management of mountain goats. Proceedings of the Biennial Symposium of the Northern Wild Sheep and Goat Council 14:5-45.

Tyers, D. B., K. L. Frey, and K. A. Gunther. 2017. History of Yellowstone grizzly bear conservation and management. Pages 177-193 in P. J. White, K. A. Gunther, F. T. van Manen, and J. A. Jerrett, editors. Yellowstone grizzly bears: ecology and conservation of an icon of wildness. Yellowstone Forever and Yellowstone National Park, Mammoth, Wyoming.

U.S. Department of Agriculture (USDA). 2017. National Agricultural Statistics Service, Montana Field Office, Helena, Montana. <http://www.nass.usda.gov/Statistics_by_State/Montana/Publications/Annual_Statistical_Bulletin/index.php>. Accessed February 5, 2018.

USDA, Forest Service. 1978. Interim direction for the Absaroka Beartooth Wilderness. Northern Region, Gallatin and Custer national forests, Bozeman, Montana.

USDA, Forest Service. 2005. Chapter 2670: threatened, endangered, and sensitive plants and animals. Forest Service manual 2600: wildlife, fish and sensitive plant habitat management. Washington, D.C.

USDA, Forest Service, and U.S. Department of Interior, Bureau of Land Management. 2015. Bighorn sheep risk of contact tool, v2 user guide. Bighorn Sheep Working Group, Washington, D.C.

U.S. Department of the Interior. 2018. Secretarial order 3362: improving habitat quality in western big game winter range and migration corridors. Washington, D.C.

Valdez, R., and P. R. Krausman. 1999. Description, distribution, and abundance of mountain sheep in North America. Pages 3-22 in R. Valdez and P. R. Krausman, editors. Mountain sheep of North America. University of Arizona Press, Tucson, Arizona.

Varley, N. C. 1994. Summer-fall habitat use and fall diets of mountain goats and bighorn sheep in the Absaroka Range, Montana. Biennial Symposium of the Northern Wild Sheep and Goat Council 9:131-138.

Varley, N. 1996. Ecology of mountain goats in the Absaroka Range, south-central Montana. Thesis, Montana State University, Bozeman, Montana.

Vaughan, R. 1900. Then and now; or thirty-six years in the Rockies. Tribune Printing Company, Minneapolis, Minnesota.

Walters, C. J. 1986. Adaptive management of renewable resources. Macmillan Publishers, Basingstoke, UK.

Waples, R. S. 2015. Testing for Hardy-Weinberg proportions: have we lost the plot? Journal of Heredity 106:1-19.

Weber, J. L., and C. Wong. 1993. Mutation of human short tandem repeats. Human Molecular Genetics 2:1123-1128.

Western Association of Fish and Wildlife Agencies. 2015. 2014 Bighorn sheep herd health monitoring recommendations. http://www.wafwa.org/Documents%20 and%20Settings/37/Site%20Documents/Working%20Groups/Wild%20Sheep/ Disease/BHS%20herd%20health%20monitoring_Final%201_3_2015.pdf.

White, K. S., and D. P. Gregovich. 2017. Mountain goat resource selection in relation to mining-related disturbance. Wildlife Biology, 2017(4) <http://dx.doi. org/10.2981/wlb.00277>.

White, K. S., D. P. Gregovich, G. W. Pendleton, N. L. Barten, A. Crupi, R. Scott, and D. N. Larsen. 2012. Modeling resource selection of mountain goats in southeastern Alaska: applications for population management and highway development planning. Biennial Symposium of the Northern Wild Sheep and Goat Council 18:32-42.

White, K. S., D. P. Gregovich, and T. Levi. 2017. Projecting the future of an alpine ungulate under climate change scenarios. Global Change Biology 24:1136-1149.

White, P. J., R. A. Garrott, and G. E. Plumb. 2013. The future of ecological process management. Pages 255-266 in P. J. White, R. A. Garrott, and G. E. Plumb, editors. Yellowstone's wildlife in transition. Harvard University Press, Cambridge, Massachusetts.

Whitfield, M. B. 1983. Bighorn sheep history, distributions and habitat relationships in the Teton Mountain Range, Wyoming. Thesis, Idaho State University, Pocatello, Idaho.

Whitfield, M. B., and B. L. Keller. 1984. Bighorn sheep of the Teton Range: ecology of a remnant population. Proceedings of the Biennial Symposium of the Northern Wild Sheep and Goat Council 4:120-136.

Whithear, K. 2001. Diseases due to mycoplasmas. Pages 413-422 in E. S. Williams and I. K. Barker, editors. Infectious diseases of wild mammals. Iowa State University Press, Ames, Iowa.

Whittlesey, L. H. 1994. Cows all over the place. The historic setting for the transmission of brucellosis to Yellowstone bison by domestic cattle. Wyoming Annals 66:42-57.

Whittlesey, L. H, and S. Bone. 2020. The history of mammals in the Greater Yellowstone Ecosystem, 1796-1881: a multi-disciplinary analysis of thousands of historical observations. Livingston, Montana.

Whittlesey, L. H., P. D. Schullery, S. Bone, A. Klein, P. J. White, A. W. Rodman, and D. E. Hallac. 2018. Using historical accounts (1796-1881) to inform contemporary wildlife management in the Yellowstone area. Natural Areas Journal 38:99-106.

Wigal, R. A., and V. L. Coggins. 1982. Mountain goat. Pages 1008-1020 in J. A. Chapman and G. A. Feldhamer, editors. Wild mammals of North America: biology, management, and economics. John Hopkins University Press, Baltimore, Maryland.

Wild Sheep Working Group. 2012. Recommendations for domestic sheep and goat management in wild sheep habitat. Western Association of Fish and Wildlife Agencies, Boise, Idaho.

Wild Sheep Working Group. 2014. Bighorn sheep: conservation challenges and management strategies for the 21st century. Western Association of Fish and Wildlife Agencies, Boise, Idaho.

Wild Sheep Working Group. 2015. Records of wild sheep translocations – United States and Canada, 1922-present. Western Association of Fish and Wildlife Agencies, Boise, Idaho.

Wilcove, D. S., and M. Wikelski. 2008. Going, going, gone: is animal migration disappearing? PLoS Biology 6.

Williams, B. K., J. D. Nichols, and M. J. Conroy. 2002. Analysis and management of animal populations. Academic Press, San Diego, California.

Williams, G. W. 2000. The USDA Forest Service: the first century. U.S. Department of Agriculture, National Forest Service, Washington, D.C.

Williams, J. S. 1999. Compensatory reproduction and dispersal in an introduced mountain goat population in central Montana. Wildlife Society Bulletin 27:1019-1024.

Wolff, P. L., T. E. Besser, D. D. Nelso, J. F. Ridpath, K. McMullen, J. Munoz-Gutierrez, M. Cox, C. Morris, and C. McAdoo. 2014. Mountain goats at the livestock-wildlife interface: a susceptible species. Biennial Symposium of the Northern Wild Sheep and Goat Council 19:13.

Wolff, P. L., J. A. Blanchong, D. D. Nelson, P. J. Plummer, C. McAdoo, M. Cox, T. E. Besser, J. Muñoz-Gutiérrez, and C. A. Anderson. 2019. Detection of *Mycoplasma ovipneumoniae* in pneumonic mountain goat (*Oreamnos americanus*) kids. Journal of Wildlife Diseases 55:206-212.

Wolff, P. L., M. Cox, C. McAdoo, and C. A. Anderson. 2016. Disease transmission between sympatric mountain goats and bighorn sheep. Proceedings of the Biennial Symposium of the Northern Wild Sheep and Goat Council 20:79.

Wood, M. E., K. A. Fox, J. Jennings-Gaines, H. J. Killion, S. Amundson, M. W. Miller, and W. H. Edwards. 2017. How respiratory pathogens contribute to lamb mortality in a poorly performing bighorn sheep (*Ovis canadensis*) herd. Journal of Wildlife Diseases 53:126-130.

Woolf, A., D. C. Kradel, and G. R. Bubash. 1970. Mycoplasma isolates from pneumonia in captive Rocky Mountain bighorn sheep. Journal of Wildlife Disease 6:169-170.

Wuerthner, G. 2017. Bighorn sheep vs domestic sheep. Wildlife News, April 11. <http://www.thewildlifenews.com/2017/04/11/bighorn-sheep-vs-domestic-sheep/>. Accessed February 14, 2018.

Wyoming Game and Fish Department. 2016. Ungulate migration corridor strategy. https://wgfd.wyo.gov/WGFD/media/ content/PDF/Habitat/Habitat%20Information/Ungulate-Migration-Corridor-Strategy_Final_020416.pdf.

Wyoming Game and Fish Department. 2018. 2018 job completion report evaluation form. Wyoming Game and Fish Department, Jackson, Wyoming. <https://wgfd.wyo.gov/WGFD/media/content/PDF/Hunting/JCRS/JCR_BGJACKSON_SHEEP_2018.pdf>.

Wyoming State-wide Bighorn Sheep-Domestic Sheep Interaction Working Group. 2004. Final report and recommendations. Wyoming Game and Fish Department, Cheyenne, Wyoming.

Young, S. P., and R. H. Manville. 1960. Records of bighorn hybrids. Journal of Mammalogy 41:523-525.

# Acknowledgments

Primary funding for this work was provided by the National Park Service (Yellowstone and Grand Teton National Parks), Canon USA Inc. via Yellowstone Forever, Wyoming Governor's Big Game License Coalition, Federal Aid in Wildlife Restoration Grant W-159-R to Montana Fish, Wildlife and Parks and the annual auction sale of a Montana bighorn sheep hunting license, Grand Teton National Park Foundation, and Greater Yellowstone Coordinating Committee, the United States Forest Service (Bridger-Teton, Shoshone, and Caribou-Targhee National Forests), and a National Science Foundation Graduate Research Fellowship. Additional funds were provided by Montana, Wyoming, and Midwest chapters of the Wild Sheep Foundation, the Wild Sheep Foundation, Idaho Safari Club International, Idaho Bureau of Land Management, Idaho Department of Fish and Game, Rocky Mountain Goat Foundation, International Order of Rocky Mountain Goats, Teton Conservation District, Wyoming Game and Fish Department, Wyoming Wildlife Livestock/Disease Research Partnership, Glacier National Park, National Geographic Society, University of Wyoming; Montana Agricultural Experiment Station, Gray Thornton, National Science Foundation Graduate Research Internship Program, and Glacier National Park Conservancy.

Scholarships and awards to undergraduate and graduate students were provided by John and Dottie Fossel, Jack Creek Preserve Foundation, Shikar Safari Club, Don C. Quimby Graduate Wildlife Research Scholarship, Wynn G. Freeman Award administered by the Montana Chapter of The Wildlife Society, Montana State University's Undergraduate Scholars Program, the Office of the Provost, and the Office of the Vice President for Research. Additional scholarships were provided by Wild Sheep Foundation and Carl and Anna Phillips through the Kevin Hurley Wild Sheep Biology Award administered by Montana State University Foundation.

State and federal agency wildlife professionals that collaborated and contributed their time and expertise included Montana Fish Wildlife and Parks: J. Cunningham, J. Gude, T. Lemke, K. Loveless, M. O'Reilly, J. Paugh, and S. Stewart; National Park

Service: J. Carpenter, C. Geremia, D. Smith, E. Stahler, J. Treanor, and T. Wyman; U.S. Fish and Wildlife Service: E. Cole, P. Hnilicka, and M. Mazure; U.S. Forest Service; U.S. Geological Survey: K. Keating; Wind River Inter-Tribal Council and Shoshone and Arapahoe Tribal Fish and Game: A. Lawson, B. Snyder, E. Brown, J. Friday, and W. Wagon; Wyoming Game and Fish: G. Anderson, B. Baker, D. Brimeyer, A. Courtemanch, T. Crane, H. Edwards, L. Ellsbury, G. Fralick, G. Gerharter, S. Harter, K. Hurley, B. Kroger, K. Lash, D. Lutz, C. Queen, C. Smith, J. Stephens, C. Timberlake, and T. Woolley. Special thanks to C. Reid, Yellowstone National Park, for providing advice and support as a contributing editor during book development.

Technical, statistical, and academic assistance was provided by Alaska Department of Fish and Game: K. White; California Department of Fish and Game: T. Stephenson; Montana Fish, Wildlife and Parks: N. DeCesare; Montana State University: C. Aasen, S. Challender, A. Litt, L. McNew, M. Sawaya, T. Paterson, and J. Thomson; National Park Service: A. Klein, L. Whittlesey, and H. Williams; Smithsonian Institution: K. Ralls; University of California Santa Cruz: J. Kapp, K. Moon, and B. Shapiro; University of Colorado: C. Lee; University of Wyoming: S. Stowell, and H. Ernest; U. S. Forest Service: C. Coffin, S. Pils, and J. Roose; U. S. Geological Survey: M. Ebinger; Washington State University: T. Besser; Western EcoSystems Technology Inc.: H. Sawyer; and M. Zambon.

Biological sample assays and laboratory support was provided by Montana Fish Wildlife and Parks: E. Almberg, N. Anderson, K. Carson, J. Ramsey, and J. Thornburg; Montana State University: J. Berardinelli, R. Lambert, V. Copié, and D. Walker; Wyoming Game and Fish: H. Edwards, J. Jennings-Gaines, and H. Killion. Field technicians that contributed to the studies included J. Cutter, M. Hockett, B. Jimenez, K. Macdonald, J. Meyer-Morey, E. Nunlist, and B. Turnock. National Park Service logistic and permitting support was provided by M. Biel, A. Carlson, S. Gunther, C. Hendrix, and K. Tonnessen, with J. Canfield and R. Feigley facilitating U.S. Forest Service logistics and permitting.

Access to private lands was provided by B-Bar, Brown-Thomas Meadow, Grizzly Creek, Mooncrest, Pitchfork, Royal Teton, Star Hill, TE, and Valley Ranches, Harry and Kathy Liss, Eric Nord, Stephen Ira, L. Stroud, and the Stillwater Mining Company. Safe and efficient helicopter animal captures were provided by Quicksilver Air Inc., Native Range Capture Services, and Leading Edge Aviation, Inc. Aerial telemetry relocation flights were conducted by Dave Stinson of Sky Aviation and Mark Packila of Wildlife Air.

The editors would like to specifically acknowledge the many photographers who donated their images to this publication; Steve Ard, Ed Arnett, Jim Berardinelli, Carson Butler, Julie Cunningham, Jesse DeVoe, Elizabeth Flesch, Sally Flesch, Jacob Frank, Mark Gocke, Adrian Sanchez Gonzalez, Stan Harter, Neal Herbert, Richard Horst, Randy Ilg, Craig Lee, Jim McLucas, Phil Merta, Jim Peaco, Chris Queen, Diane Renkin, Joe Riis, Craig Sax, Dan Stahler, Shawn T. Stewart, Kenneth R. Whitten, and Travis Zaffarano.

Special thanks to Lorelyn Mayr of Media Works LLC, Bozeman, Montana for her expertise, advice, and patience in preparing the book manuscript for publication.

# Author Affiliations

Carson J. Butler, National Park Service, Grand Teton National Park, Moose, Wyoming

Julie A. Cunningham, Montana Fish, Wildlife and Parks, Bozeman, Montana

Jesse D. DeVoe, Department of Ecology, Montana State University, Bozeman, Montana

Sarah R. Dewey, National Park Service, Grand Teton National Park, Moose, Wyoming

Elizabeth P. Flesch, Department of Ecology, Montana State University, Bozeman, Montana

Robert A. Garrott, Department of Ecology, Montana State University, Bozeman, Montana

Tabitha A. Graves, U.S. Geological Survey, Northern Rocky Mountain Science Center, West Glacier, Montana

Blake Lowrey, Department of Ecology, Montana State University, Bozeman, Montana

Douglas E. McWhirter, Wyoming Game and Fish Department, Jackson, Wyoming

Hollie M. Miyasaki, Idaho Department of Fish and Game, Idaho Falls, Idaho

Kevin Monteith, Department of Zoology and Physiology, University of Wyoming, Laramie, Wyoming

Kerry M. Murphy, U.S. Forest Service, Shoshone National Forest, Cody, Wyoming

Andrew C. Pils, U.S. Forest Service, Shoshone National Forest, Cody, Wyoming

Kelly M. Proffitt, Montana Fish, Wildlife and Parks, Bozeman, Montana

246    Jay J. Rotella, Department of Ecology, Montana State University, Bozeman, Montana

Daniel B. Tyers, U.S. Forest Service, Custer Gallatin National Forest, Bozeman, Montana

P. J. White, National Park Service, Yellowstone National Park, Mammoth, Wyoming

Mary E. Wood, Colorado Parks and Wildlife, Fort Collins, Colorado

# Index

## I

**K**

Kids: birth/nursing of, 7, 17 and 77; disease, 214 and 240; groups, 12, 53, 103, and 204; growth rates, 17; mortality, 17 and 214; predation on, 78 and 148; and recruitment, 150-151.

**L**

Lactation: costs of, 77 and 144; milk production, 17 and 77; salt licks, 56 and 77; timing of, 12, 77, 138, and 143; weaning, 119, 138, and 143; and weather effects on, 17 and 138.

Lambs: birth of, 7, 71, 77, 138-139, and 143; disease effects on, 5, 7, 37, 111-114, 121-122, 156, 234, and 240; learning, 67 and 70-71; predation on, 7-9, 37, 50, 78, and 148; and weather and climate effects on, 7, 138-139, and 232.

Landscapes, 45, 47, 49, 53-54, 57, 59, 61, 71, 73-74, 78-81, 94, 118, 123, 126, 133-134, 144-147, 152-153, 157-158, 170, 174-175, 177, 179-182, 197, 202, 208, 211, 225, 228, and 236.

Land use. *See* Human land use practices.

Learning: how we learn, 42-43, 62-63, 82-85, 108-109, 130-131, 159-161, 180-183, and 210-211; mountain ungulates, 66-67, 70, 74, 78, and 225.

Licks (salt and trace minerals), 15, 46, 55-58, 73, 76-78, 165-166, 213, 223, 231, and 235.

Livestock: cattle, 1, 26, 29, 38, 114-115, 119, and 239; goats (domestic), 5, 214, and 220; grazing, 2, 8, 10, 29-31, 33-34, 38, 41, 59, 90, 120, 126, 155, 189, 192-193, and 204; horses, 25, 29, 97, and 201-202; llamas, 6; and sheep (domestic), 2, 5-6, 8, 10, 29-34, 38, 89-92, 94, 106, 112-113, 118, 120-122, 155, 176-177, 189, 192-194, 204-205, 214, 221, 225, 228, 230, 234, and 239-241.

**M**

Madison Range, 34, 121, 133, 137, 152, 154, 170, 196-197, 206, and 208.

Management: adaptive, 188; controversy over, 61, 158, 208, and 211; definition, 186; disease, 8, 20, 111, 113-117, 119-120, 130-131, 164-165, 172, 175-176, 178, 189, 192-194, and 202; funding, 194-195; genetics, 88 and 93-106; habitat, 47, 173, 178, 189-192, and 207; hunting, 8, 20, 47, 148, 174-177, 188-189, 194-195, 200, 202, 205, 207, and 211; issues regarding, xiv, 61, 147-148, 158, 164-165, 172-179, 205, 208, 211, and 215; jurisdictions, 2, 21, 33, 61, 137-138, 148, 173-175, 185-189, 205, and 211; metapopulations, 10, 152-153, 196-197, and 207; models, 48 and 185; migration corridors, 78, 80, and 82-85; monitoring